The
Wild Flowering Pl
of Bahrain

Half title *Cassia italica*
Facing title page *Aeluropus littoralis*
Contents *Convolvulus pilosellifolius*
Last page *Portulaca oleracea*

The
Wild Flowering Plants
of Bahrain
An Illustrated Guide

M.D. and C.D. Cornes

IMMEL
Publishing

CONTENT

As will be noted from Chapter 3, the author completed general flora surveys in most localities on Bahrain, Muharraq, Nabih Salih and Sitra islands over a period of 5 years in all seasons, collecting specimens for Edinburgh Royal Botanic Garden from various communities for nearly 3 years.

Descriptions in Section III stem from her studies of the plants and specimens and their associated species and habitats, and were checked for botanical accuracy by Dr. I. Hedge at Edinburgh Royal Botanic Garden. Names for plants described came from the specimens, identified by staff at Kew Royal Botanic Gardens (some grasses) and Edinburgh. The author's catalogue numbers on specimens kept at Edinburgh Herbarium are cited with texts. Those for which firm determinations were not available in time for printing have been designated 'provisional determination', 'identified by author' or 'species' as appropriate. In order to make the guide as complete as possible, species not found by the author have been included and indicated in the text by the initials of the collector or source of information. Information sources were such publications and papers as were available, collector Mrs. M. Alder and, for Cruciferae, Edinburgh Herbarium.

Responsibility for naming photographs lies entirely with the author.

First published in Great Britain by
Immel Publishing Limited
Ely House,
37 Dover Street,
London W1X 3RB

Designed by Pat Craddock
Maps, charts and diagrams drawn by Liz Hubbard
Phototypeset in Plantin with Palatino for display
by V.I.P. Type Limited, Milton Keynes
Printed and bound in Singapore
by Tien Wah Press (Pte) Ltd.

British Library Cataloguing in Publication Data
Cornes, M. D.
  The wild flowering plants of Bahrain.
  1. Bahrain. Flowering plants.
  I. Title II. Cornes, C. D.
  582.13'0953'65
  ISBN 0-907151-41-8

Aizoon canariense

Foreword

Anyone who has ventured into the desert regions of Bahrain's unique landscape will have encountered its fascinating plantlife. Many of our attractive wild flowers exhibit ingenious adaptations enabling them to survive where few species can endure the combination of arid conditions, temperature extremes and salt-ridden soils characterising much of the island's territory. The pleasure of exploring Bahrain's desert or semi-desert regions and discovering for oneself the subtle beauty of the wild flowering plants, is one which we encountered growing up here. I have long felt the need for a comprehensive, scientifically accurate and well illustrated text on the subject. I was particularly pleased to encourage the authors of this book in the pursuit of their ambition to create a readable and useful guide to Bahrain's wildflowers and I congratulate them on their efforts.

This book, the first of its kind for Bahrain, describes two hundred and fifty four species found here. The authors have created a comprehensive identification guide together with a readable and interesting text in which they have focused upon ecological and behavioural aspects of our plant life. The importance of such a work goes far beyond the immediate function of providing a valuable source of reference for amateur and professional naturalists. It is also an important reminder that Bahrain's natural environment deserves our care in ensuring that its wild life is protected and that unique areas remain undisturbed. I am sure that the book will play a role in helping us to increase environmental awareness in Bahrain and to provide the protection which our wild flora will need in the years ahead.

I sincerely hope that this book will encourage both visitors and residents to take a closer interest in the wild flowering plants of Bahrain.

TARIQ A. ALMOAYED
Minister of Information

Introduction

It is hoped that this book will help bring the desert to life for readers who imagine it to be a barren place and take all readers beyond looking and observing; that it will help bring them to a sense of belonging in natural surroundings and to benefit from participation in the non-contrived harmony of the natural world.

The desert, with its stark and lonely beauty, seems to possess a timelessness and peace wrought of a seeming lack of fecundity, but during daylight hours of relentless shimmering heat with instinct turned solely toward survival most life is merely hidden, awaiting the magical dusk when cooling rocks and sand are bathed in a mellow glow and night breezes gently stir dry grass tussocks in their soughing quest across the plains. Plants cannot hide, however, and had to adapt for survival.

Glistening cylinders, shining spheres, translucent filaments; science fiction? vegetation on an alien planet? – none of these, but desert plants with fascinating adaptations for survival in a harsh environment. An attractive subject, but one with too little available information and literature, especially in Bahrain. In this age of high technology, with its mass-produced medicines and foods and synthetic materials, much everyday plant lore has been forgotten and lost. Plant life, which is after all the very essence of human existence on earth, must be respected and preserved, and it is to be hoped that, in future times, the reservation in Al Areen Wildlife Park will not be the only remaining habitat for the flora of Bahrain. Recognition and identification of plants with the help of books such as this will lead to knowledge and caring, then to awareness of the respect people owe their greatest heritage, the environment.

M. D. Cornes.

1986

CONTENTS

Acknowledgements

The interest and help invested in the publication of this book by H.E. Tariq Almoayed, Minister of Information for Bahrain, is gratefully acknowledged. Grateful thanks are also due to Mr. J.S. Bell, Director-General Public Security, Ministry of the Interior, for granting passes allowing access to the south of Bahrain island for flora and fauna surveys and permitting the Al Areen/ Bahrain Natural History Society conservation team to visit the Hawar Islands in early 1983; to Lt. Colonel Abdul Aziz Attiyatullah Al Khalifa, Director Coastguard Directorate for assisting in conveying the team to Hawar and the Public Security Force and Bahrain Defence Force for assistance on Hawar.

Also gratefully acknowledged is invaluable help in obtaining various books and encouragement and advice freely given by Dr. A.K. AlKhalili, Gulf University; interest and help from Barrie Webb, Webb Construction, without which work could not have been completed; and interest, advice and encouragement from Dr. I. Hedge and Mrs. R. King at Edinburgh Royal Botanic Garden and Dr. T. Cope at Kew Royal Botanic Gardens; Dr. I. Hedge kindly read through the plant descriptions making corrections and suggestions for improvement; staff at Edinburgh and Kew (grasses) provided names for most plants. Acknowledged with thanks are interest and help from Sheikh Hamad bin Abdulla Al Khalifa, Assistant Under Secretary, Civil Aviation, Majeed Isa, Deputy Senior Meteorological Officer and Abdul Rahman in the Climatological Office in providing weather information; Professor M.O. Abdel-Rahman, Scientific and Applied Research Department, University of Qatar, offering advice and donating a valuable study book; David Hunt, mammologist at Al Areen Wildlife Park, lending books and permitting access to Al Areen; Professor L. Boulos, Faculty of Science, University of Kuwait, donating a valuable study book; and Mr. J.M. Mullin, Botanical Society of the British Isles; also helpful suggestions from Maureen Truscott, Bahrain Natural History Society member; background support, especially on flora forays and at slide talks, from numerous members of B.N.H.S.; invaluable work by B.N.H.S. members, past and present, resulting in publication of flora records in society biennial reports, especially collecting and recording by K.J. Virgo and Don Bellamy and collecting by Margaret Alder; encouragement and help in arranging visits to Al Areen Wildlife Park from Edward Allonby at Al Areen; liaison with publisher by Susan Cornes; help from Gavin Cornes in photographing specimens and coming out on forays and to photograph plants when asked; and help and support from Chris Cornes who came out whenever requested to photograph plants, sometimes twice in one day, often in extreme temperatures and without whose endeavours and encouragement this book would never have been produced.

M. Cornes

1987

Picture Credits

بِسْمِ ٱللَّهِ ٱلرَّحْمَٰنِ ٱلرَّحِيمِ

وَهُوَ ٱلَّذِىٓ أَنزَلَ مِنَ ٱلسَّمَآءِ مَآءً

فَأَخْرَجْنَا بِهِۦ نَبَاتَ كُلِّ شَىْءٍ فَأَخْرَجْنَا مِنْهُ خَضِرًا نُّخْرِجُ مِنْهُ

حَبًّا مُّتَرَاكِبًا وَمِنَ ٱلنَّخْلِ مِن طَلْعِهَا قِنْوَانٌ دَانِيَةٌ وَجَنَّٰتٍ

مِّنْ أَعْنَابٍ وَٱلزَّيْتُونَ وَٱلرُّمَّانَ مُشْتَبِهًا وَغَيْرَ مُتَشَٰبِهٍ

ٱنظُرُوٓا۟ إِلَىٰ ثَمَرِهِۦٓ إِذَآ أَثْمَرَ وَيَنْعِهِۦٓ إِنَّ فِى ذَٰلِكُمْ لَءَايَٰتٍ

لِّقَوْمٍ يُؤْمِنُونَ ﴿٩٩﴾   الانعام ٩٩

In the name of God
Most Gracious, Most Merciful

It is He who sendeth down water from the sky and
therewith We produce vegetation of all kinds;
We bring forth green shoots from which We produce grain,
heaped up, and out of the date-palm and its spathes
spring clusters of dates hanging low and near;
also there are gardens of vines, and the olive
and the pomegranate, alike and unlike.
Look upon the fruit thereof when they bear fruit,
and upon its ripening.
Behold! in these things there are signs for
a people who believe.

Extracted from the Glorious Quraan,
Surah VI: Al-An A'am (The Cattle),
verses: 99
Translation, Dr. A. K. AlKhalili

I

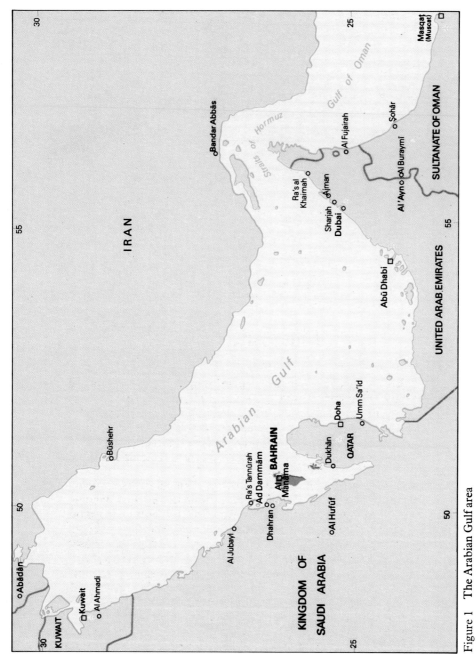

Figure 1   The Arabian Gulf area
Adapted from Map of Bahrain, published by the Ministry of Information, Bahrain.

14

Nabih Salih Island

The Land

Bahrain is a pale hazy island, crowned in the north by a grey-green swath of date palm plantations, gardens and fields. Southwards, *al barr*, lies flat stony desert relieved by a few gentle hills and escarpments and dotted with rounded scrub bushes. Then bands of sand and darker *sabkha* with their blobs of vegetation, often perceived through the brilliant heat's dazzle as mirages – icebergs and islands mysteriously suspended in soft cerulean seas, narrow into a long sand spit at the island's southern tip.

With a maximum length of 40km. and breadth of 15km. at its widest point, Bahrain is the largest of a group of islands constituting the State of Bahrain. The archipelago lies about half way along the Arabian Gulf, north-west of the Qatar peninsular and 25km. from the east coast of Saudi Arabia, at approximately 26°N x 50°35′E. (Fig. 1) Three of the smaller islands, Muharraq at Bahrain's north-eastern tip, and Nabih Salih and Sitra off the east coast, lie so close they function as part of the main island, being linked to it by dual carriageway bridges. (Fig. 3) The uninhabited islands Jazirat Hawar, Suwad Al Janubiyah, Suwad ash Shamatiyah and Umm Kharurah together with about 12 islets lie 4½ hours by dhow to the south-east of Bahrain.

A population of approximately 360,000, including over 75,000 foreign nationals, reside and work in Bahrain's busy modern capital, Manama, (Fig. 3),the three other principal towns of Muharraq, Isa Town and Hamad Town and various villages scattered along the north coastal strip and extending to about halfway down the west and east coasts.

Traditionally an important commerce and travel centre, Bahrain has been identified as the island from which merchants of the legendary Dilmun civilisation traded with peoples of the Indus Valley, Oman and Mesopotamia during the 3rd. and 2nd. millenia B.C. The famous Bahrain pearls were exported in those times, and the pearl fishing industry prospered until the first half of this century. Oil was discovered in 1931 and thus was the terrain as well as the economy transformed.

The islands are flat, rising almost imperceptibly from the shallow waters of the gulf. Bahrain island is formed from an anticlinal dome of sedimentary limestone rocks. Much of its centre has been displaced, however, creating a long shallow saucer, the **central depression**, some 10km. long by 2.5km. wide. This is encircled by inward-facing scarps up to about 20m. high formed from the remaining rock strata and called the **rim rock**. Outwardly the **back-slope** shelves gently down from the rim rock to the **coastal region**. (Fig. 3) All that remains of the summit of the dome is a ridge of hills in the central depression, of which **Jebel Dukhan**, rising to a height of 134m. above sea-level, is its highest point. Harsh sunlight, sand-laden winds and, to a lesser extent, water weather the rock so that the hillsides and backslopes are composed of crumbling rock pavements, boulders and small screes. These are interwoven with *wadis* and gullies through which are washed and deposited the finer products of erosion, sand, sediment particles and stone fragments. There are many flint stones among the pieces of chert and limestone. This detritus fans onto the central depression and coastal region respectively, forming flat or slightly undulating plains of consolidated stony or gravelly sand and sediment. *Aeolian* sands in the form of thin sheets, hummocks or very small dunes cover quite extensive areas of the plains. Salt flats *(sabkha)* occupy much of the coast and low-lying southern central depression. The island is bordered by a narrow strip of marine sand. Freshwater springs, from reservoirs of ground water trapped between impermeable layers in the rock strata, arise on land and in the sea around Bahrain. These subterranean reservoirs, fed by a vast aquifer beneath Saudi Arabia and extending to the Arabian Gulf, are Bahrain's main water resource.

Climate and Adaptation by Plants

Hot-desert climates are characterised by high temperatures and erratic, often scanty rainfall. Add to these factors high relative humidity and the result is Bahrain's notorious climate. Temperatures in coastal areas and islands rarely soar like those of inland regions, but daytime relative humidity remains high and summer day temperatures of maybe 38°C accompanied by 50% relative humidity, as experienced on Bahrain, are extremely taxing to humans. The cooler months from December to March are quite pleasant, however.

Air temperature
Long-term records, over a 39 year period to December 1984, show mean daily maximum temperatures ranged from 29.1°C for April to 37.6°C for August and 27.5°C for November; the highest temperature recorded was 46.7°C in May 1972. For the cooler months mean daily maxima were 22°C for December, 19.9°C for January and 24.5°C for March, with a lowest maximum of 7.8°C occurring in January 1964; the lowest minimum of 2.8°C occurred on the same day.

Relative humidity

Night-time relative humidity in the region of 90-100% is not uncommon. Long-term (1958-1984) mean daily maxima for February and October were respectively 88% and 89%; mean daily minima for those months were 56% and 46%. August, usually the most uncomfortable month, shows a mean daily maximum of 84% and minimum of 44%.

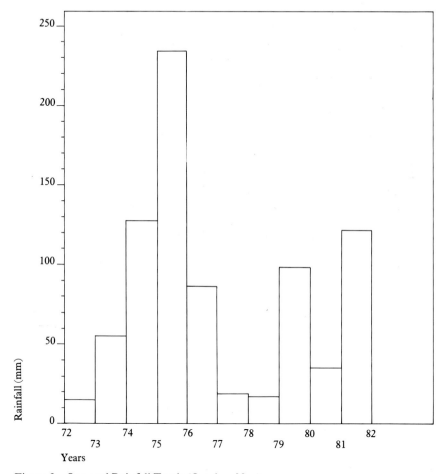

Figure 2   Seasonal Rainfall Totals (October-May)

Rainfall

The ten-year chart (fig. 2) showing seasonal rainfall totals illustrates that, although rain does fall regularly, amounts of precipitation vary considerably from year to year and may be extremely scant. Averages range from 234mm, October 1975 – May 1976 to as low as 15mm, October 1959 – May 1960 and 1972 – 1973. Over 38 years to 1983, January had the highest mean monthly rainfall of 18mm and highest rainfall in one month, of 135.9mm, in 1959. However, April had the highest in one day, a record 64mm, in 1961. August shows nil rain over the 38 years; June, July and September had negligible amounts of less than .05mm but more than zero. The longest drought on record in Bahrain ended with a thunderstorm on 27th. February, 1984 after 319 rainless days.

17

A rare sight – clouds ! and the southern central depression under water after exceptional rainfall, 1983

Wind
Bahrain lies in the path of north-westerlies known as shamal winds, which blow most of the year and though persistent, rarely become unpleasant. Light to moderate breezes are normal, with winds sometimes reaching strong gale force during winter. The highest gust speed recorded in recent years was 51 knots. There are occasional dust storms and at times, during summer, an extremely oppressive wind from the south-east, but Bahrain's high temperatures are mainly tempered by the prevailing winds.

Vegetation
While it is generally known and accepted that deserts bloom dramatically after a shower of rain, surprise or disbelief may be expressed that perennial desert plants possess the ability not only to survive but also to sustain green living parts, flowers even, during prolonged rainless periods. The main problem for desert plants, that of maintaining a balance between water uptake and water loss, essential for healthy growth and indeed for survival, is well demonstrated on Bahrain. Fierce radiant heat, hot desiccating winds and lack of moisture in the ground create a harsh environment but the plants have adapted to these climatic conditions, which accounts for some of their strange fascinating forms.

Plants **without special adaptations to environmental extremes**, termed **mesophytes**, are found in areas with irrigation or fresh-water streams, mainly in the north of Bahrain.

Xerophytes, drought resisters, constitute the sparse perennial vegetative cover on Bahrain outside irrigated zones.

Halophytes, adapted to **tolerate saline soils**, may be included with this group. The characteristic salinity of desert soils is worsened by lack of rain and accelerated evaporation to a degree damaging to most plants in many areas. Salt-secreting halophytes are able to rid themselves of excess salts through special salt-glands in their leaves and stems, e.g. *Tamarix* spp., *Limonium axillare* and *Atriplex leucoclada*. The presence of high salt levels within plants is sometimes manifest by red coloration, e.g. *Frankenia pulverulenta* and *Suaeda* spp. Many halophytes possess succulent parts in which they store salts, e.g. *Zygophyllum qatarense*, *Salsola baryosma* and *Halocnemum strobilaceum*. True halophytes, however, are found by the sea where they withstand occasional or twice-daily swamping by high tides, e.g. *Suaeda maritima* and *Arthrocnemum* spp.

Mechanisms evolved by xerophytes which help them avoid heat damage and moisture loss and prevent wilting include:

a) **Reduction of surface area** lessening exposure to solar radiation and hot winds thus reducing transpiration, achieved by:

1) Possession of minute leaves, e.g. *Tamarix* spp; linear leaves, e.g. *Leptadenia pyrotechnica* and *Ochradenus baccatus*.
2) Leaf-shedding at commencement of dry season, e.g. *Lycium shawii* and *Zygophyllum qatarense*. *Z. qatarense* sheds leaves and branches after winters of particularly scanty rainfall.
3) Leaves rolled edge to edge in grasses, e.g. *Stipagrostis* spp.
4) Folded leaflets, e.g. *Prosopis juliflora* and *Cassia italica*.
5) Rolled leaf margins, e.g. *Teucrium polium* and *Helianthemum* spp.
6) Production of spines formed from modified leaves and stipules, e.g. *Acacia* species, and thorns from reduced modified branches, e.g. *Lycium shawii*.

b) **Protection** by spines, hairs or bristles on above-ground parts which reflect heat and inhibit transpiration/evaporation, e.g. *Cornulaca monacantha* (spines) *Heliotropium ramosissimum* (bristly hairs) and *Aerva javanica* (dense short hairs). Many species have leathery leaves with a thick cuticle and epidermis, e.g. *Ziziphus nummularia*.

c) **Efficient moisture absorption** aided by development of extensive root systems with high root to shoot ratio. Examples:

1) *Monsonia nivea* – depth and thickness of root enormous compared with above-ground dimensions of plant.
2) *Acacia* and *Prosopis* spp. – develop dual systems of long tap roots reaching to water far below the surface and horizontal roots just beneath the surface to catch moisture from rain showers.
3) Grasses – have networks of roots just below the surface to exploit small amounts of moisture from dew and light showers.
4) *Erodium glaucophyllum* – has thickened root sections for storage of moisture and nutrients; observed with green leaves after months without rain.

The open nature of plant cover in deserts means lack of competition between root systems for meagre moisture supplies but prevents plants sheltering or shading each other above ground. A prostrate or low-growing habit, adopted by many plants, helps prevent evaporation of precious moisture from the soil.

Therophytes, drought evaders, are annuals appearing briefly after rain has fallen and only while surface moisture is available, e.g. *Trigonella stellata*. Some are termed ephemeral, so brief is their life cycle, e.g. *Senecio* spp. Seeds of annuals and ephemerals lie dormant during much of the year (even longer when necessary) awaiting rainfall, as they require adequate amounts of rain for successful growth. Though possibly considered less well adapted to arid conditions than xerophytes because they avoid drought altogether, they nonetheless possess instant response to moisture, e.g. *Mesembryanthemum* spp. and *Anastatica hierochuntica*, and the ability to germinate, flower and produce seeds in large quantities within a remarkably short space of time. Seed capsules of *Mesembryanthemum* spp. have apical triangular flaps which spring open on contact with water, and the seeds of *Anastatica hierochuntica* remain protected within curled woody stems until the presence of moisture in sufficient amounts causes them to rapidly uncurl and release seeds.

Plants will regulate their size in accordance with prevailing conditions, e.g. in February 1983 roadsides, depressions and *wadis* were carpeted with *Asphodelus fistulosus* after abundant rainfall during the preceding December and January. The following year only a few small *Asphodelus*, a quarter of normal size, appeared in late April after a dry winter with scant rain until March.

Plant distribution is influenced by wind force and direction, thus a distinct NW-SE drift is apparent on Bahrain. Wind conveys topsoil and distributes pollen and seeds. Plants with plumed or tufted seeds dispersed by this means are particularly successful, e.g. *Stipagrostis* spp., *Erodium glaucophyllum* and Compositae. Wind-borne sand and particles lodge in hollows and *wadis* and against rocks creating favourable sites for germinating seeds.

Wadi after flash flood, 1983

The key factor affecting growth in Bahrain's desert plants is rainfall. Water pouring from high places is a sculptor, carving gullies and runnels while transporting products of erosion and seeds. Typical desert down-pours give rise to flash floods which roar through *wadis* then fan onto the plains depositing along their way stones, gravel, sand, fine sediments and seeds. *Wadis* may appear ravaged after such inundations but vegetation, taking advantage of rich deposits left behind, swiftly becomes re-established. Perennial and annual plants favour sites to which water gravitates so their distribution and density follow and mark the land's topography, which was itself shaped by wind and water.

Plant Habitats and Associations and Effects of Human Activities

The flora of Bahrain reflects the island's geographical position and land area of about 600km². Its plant community mainly comprises a small but varied selection of species representative of the Saharo-Sindian* flora region. Also present are typical Mediterranean and Irano-Turanian species and one or two introduced (weed) species from N. and S. America.

Topography influences character and distribution of vegetation and, although on Bahrain none of the physiographic factors involved are extremely pronounced, various habitats are discernible in which distinct plant associations occur. It is helpful and of interest to be able to locate the habitats and thereby recognise their associated plant species.

The coastal region may be divided into two zones:
1) **Inhabited zone**, ie. urban, village and industrial areas and land under cultivation where irrigation is practised, chiefly in the north but extending along the N.W. and N.E. coasts. Soils are characteristically sandy, calcareous and saline, often gypsic, with high saline water-table levels. In habitats without irrigation the dominant plant is perennial shrub *Suaeda vermiculata*. It forms dense thickets on abandoned plantations, among natural date palm (*Phoenix dactylifera*) communities and around fields. Also prominent in open spaces and along roads are halophytic herb, *Cressa cretica* and spiny shrublet, *Alhagi maurorum*. The shrub *Capparis spinosa* should be mentioned as it is becoming quite common in these areas. Great screens of reed grass, *Phragmites australis*, arise along borders of streams and ditches. Communities in low-lying salines are dominated by *Aeluropus lagopoides*; associates include *Sporobolus arabicus* and *Limonium axillare*.

Dwarf mangrove (*Avicennia marina*) and *Suaeda maritima* by Sanad

The muddy littoral shoreline and coastal marshes along the N.E. coast between Ras Tubli and Ras Ikur support colonies of dwarf mangrove

* The Saharo-Sindian region extends from the coast of N.W. Africa across the Sahara, Sinai, extra- tropical Arabia, southern Iraq and Iran to the deserts of northern India.

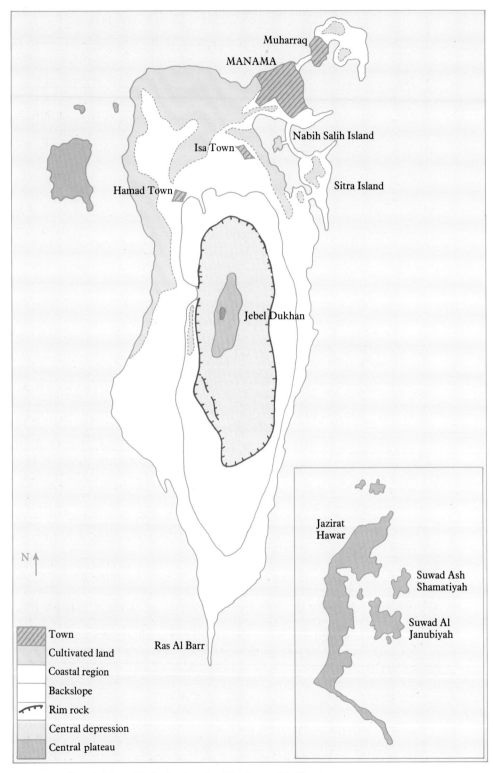

Figure 3   Sketch Map of Bahrain showing Physiographic Zones

(*Avicennia marina*), *Arthrocnemum salicornicum* and *Suaeda maritima*. Other important species in this halophytic community include *Arthrocnemum macrostachyum*, *Phragmites australis*, *Juncus rigidus* and *Aeluropus littoralis*; dense growth of the grass *Aeluropus littoralis* occurs on banks of drainage channels west of Tubli. *Halocnemum strobilaceum*, *Suaeda vermiculata* and parasite *Cistanche tubulosa* occur on the N.E. shoreline in habitats without frequent inundation by high tides. Around Salmabad soils are saline with high water-table and poor drainage; *Halocnemum strobilaceum* is the dominant plant in association with *Aeluropus lagopoides*, giving way in places to *Juncus rigidus* and small stands of *Phragmites australis*. North-east of Aali village this community merges with vegetation typical of long-abandoned fields and occupying much of the land from Aali to Hamalah and Dumistan; soil is gypsic and often saline. *Suaeda vermiculata* is prominent in this habitat with associated species *Anabasis setifera*, *Zygophyllum qatarense*, *Limonium axillare*, *Launaea nudicaulis*, *Atriplex leucoclada*, *Aeluropus lagopoides* and *Sporobolus arabicus*. Soil in date plantations, fields and gardens is loamy and has relatively low salinity. Weed species in these areas include:

Phyla nodiflora	*Mesembryanthemum nodiflorum*
Convolvulus arvensis	*Sesuvium verrucosum*
Heliotropium currasavicum	*Frankenia pulverulenta*
Melilotus indica	*Cynodon dactylon*
Chenopodium murale	*Polypogon monspeliensis*
Amaranthus graecizans	*Launaea procumbens*
Spergularia bocconii	*Sonchus oleraceus*

Particularly prominent around margins of fields and habitations are the shrub *Salsola baryosma* and fleshy herb *Sesuvium verrucosum*. These species are also in evidence along roadsides with *Suaeda aegyptiaca* and *Suaeda vermiculata*. Clusters of ephemeral, *Senecio glaucus* border roads after rain. Some abandoned fields with impoverished stony soils are colonised by dwarf shrub *Prosopis farcta*. *Heliotropium ramosissimum* is the dominant plant in a sand sheet south-west of Sar and in patches of wind-blown sand. After rain *Cistanche tubulosa* (Desert hyacinth) appears in abundance on farmland north-east of Dumistan, parasitic on *Zygophyllum qatarense*. *Phoenix dactylifera* and *Prosopis juliflora* trees appear singly or in small stands throughout this zone. More sporadic, in salines and patches of *sabkha*, are bushy *Tamarix arabica*.

There remain no completely natural plant communities in this zone, although apparently some of the original species have recolonised long-abandoned fields and plantations. Trampling, grazing and browsing at will by livestock, however, often keeps growth of palatable species to a minimum. (Herds of sheep, goats and camels create particular problems, including loss of perennials leading to soil erosion, in the central depression where plant cover is normally sparse.) Lack of vegetation and competition for meagre food supplies results in declining numbers of lizards, insects and other fauna. Alfalfa (*Medicago sativa*) is grown to feed livestock, and a scheme has just been initiated whereby treated sewage is utilised in production of fodder-grass.

Plentiful fresh water for domestic and agricultural purposes was formerly obtained from the once famous natural Bahrain springs and surface wells, but artesian wells were drilled ever deeper as industry developed, demand for fresh water increased and water at higher levels became brackish. Demand has overtaken replenishment; the resulting decline in ground

Alfalfa (*Medicago sativa*) and
vegetables growing in shade
of date palms (*Phoenix dactylifera*)

Sabkha with *Halocnemum strobilaceum* and
Halopeplis perfoliata

water levels has aggravated aridity, caused springs to dry up and allows increasing infiltration by salt water into the supply, leading to salinization of the soil.

Industrial development is centred on the north-east and in this area the delicate balance of mangrove-swamp ecology is being destroyed by land reclamation, dredging, pollution and construction. Construction of dual carriageways and urban and industrial sites have eradicated vegetation from large tracts of land. However, ornamental trees and shrubs have been planted along roads and in parks and gardens, including *Tamarix aphylla*, *Prosopis juliflora*, *Ricinus communis* and *Eucalyptus*, *Nerium* (Oleander), *Sesbania* and *Bougainvillea* species. Fruit trees include *Ziziphus spina-christi*, *Pithecellobium dulce*, *Amygdalus* sp. (Almond), *Pumica granatum* (Pomegranate), *Phoenix dactylifera* (Date Palm), *Citrus* species (Lemon and Citron), *Ficus* sp. (Fig) and *Morus nigra* (Black mulberry).

2) Southern coastal zone

Plant cover diminishes toward the south, vegetation mainly comprising sparse low shrubs and perennial grasses. Soil is calcareous, often gypsic, generally saline with high water-table. The east coastal strip between back-slope and beach is narrow and only one section of coast remains undisturbed. Here, in *sabkha* adjoining the beach, succulent-leaved halophyte *Halopeplis perfoliata* is the dominant plant with associates *Arthrocnemum macrostachyum*, *Halocnemum strobilaceum* and *Suaeda vermiculata*. Adjacent to this an *Aeluropus lagopoides* – *Zygophyllum qatarense* association can be seen with *Sporobolus arabicus*, *Limonium axillare* and *Anabasis setifera*. There are stands of sedge *Cyperus conglomeratus* in sand deposits near the beach. Beyond the southern backslope is a gradually diminishing *Zygophyllum qatarense* – *Aeluropus lagopoides* community with wind and water-borne sand forming hummocks against the vegetation.

This is flanked on its eastern side by a broad band of *sabkha* supporting *Halopeplis perfoliata* and *Halocnemum strobilaceum*. *H. strobilaceum* gathers wind and water-borne soil into a mound around its stems. The *sabkha* narrows towards the southern tip of the island, Ras Al Barr, where *Seidlitzia rosmarinus* and *Arthrocnemum macrostachyum* flourish on and among small sand dunes.

1   *Seidlitzia rosmarinus-Arthrocnemum macrostachyum* community at Ras Al Barr

2   Southern *sabkha* with mirage

3   *Heliotropium ramosissimum-Cyperus conglomeratus* community on small dunes near Ras Noma

4   Western *wadi* with broom bushes (*Leptadenia pyrotechnica*)

Dunes with *Seidlitzia rosmarinus* bushes continue northwards along the south-west coast with *Cyperus conglomeratus*, scattered *Suaeda vermiculata* and *Limonium axillare* appearing in a gravelly sand belt next to the dunes.

Seidlitzia rosmarinus becomes sparse as the land widens. Broad areas of *sabkha* and sand-hummocks appear. *Halopeplis perfoliata* grows in the *sabkha*, while *Zygophyllum qatarense* predominates in the inland hummock-sand area; other species are sparse and stunted. Continuing northward, much of the terrain is occupied by the western sand-sheets.

Soil in this habitat is less saline and supports more varied vegetation. *Heliotropium ramosissimum* and *Pennisetum divisum* are the dominant species, with associates including *Panicum turgidum, Polycarpaea repens, Moltkiopsis ciliata, Monsonia nivea, Cyperus conglomeratus, Calligonum polygonoides, Leptadenia pyrotechnica, Helianthemum lippii* and *Cynomorium coccineum*, parasitising on *Zygophyllum qatarense*. Large quantities of sand are regularly removed from this area for agricultural and local construction purposes. *Sabkhas* border beaches along the west coast, some being devoid of plant cover while in others the only vegetation is *Zygophyllum qatarense*; halophytic grasses *Aeluropus lagopoides* and *Sporobolus arabicus* appear in *sabkha* with salt crust.

The backslope offers varied habitats from *wadis* with deep wind-borne sand deposits to microhabitats in crevices in bare rock slabs. The former, providing some of the most pleasant natural surroundings on the island, occur in the western backslope. Fine examples of the tall shrub *Leptadenia pyrotechnica* abound with large tussocks of perennial grasses *Pennisetum divisum* and *Panicum turgidum* and stands of *Cyperus conglomeratus*. *Leptadenia pyrotechnica* is the sole plant in deep sand drifts. *Calligonum polygonoides* appears in western and south-western gullies and *wadis* with shallower sand deposits; associates include *Zygophyllum qatarense*, parasite *Cynomorium coccineum* and annual lily *Asphodelus fistulosus*.

A large shallow *wadi* on the north-west backslope affords a rich vegetation in which most Bahrain desert plants are represented. Soils, ranging from stony gravelly sand to fine sediment, contain wind and water-borne material. *Ziziphus nummularia* forms dense thickets bordered by *Salsola baryosma*, *Atriplex leucoclada* and *Suaeda vermiculata*. *Lycium shawii, Anabasis setifera* and grasses *Dichanthium annulatum, Eremopogon foveolatus* and *Cymbopogon* species are prominent and other species include:

Heliotropium kotschyi	*Atractylis flava*
Fagonia bruguieri	*Pulicaria species*
Zygophyllum qatarense	*Sclerocephalus arabicus*
Helianthemum species	*Convolvulus pilosellifolius*
Andrachne telephioides	*Teucrium polium*
Herniaria hemistemon	*Farsetia heliophila*
Salvia aegyptiaca	*Scrophularia deserti*
Launaea species	*Prosopis juliflora*

Annuals include: *Zygophyllum simplex*
Trigonella stellata
Aizoon canariense
Anastatica hierochuntica

Small gravelly *wadis* in the west and north-west contain *Zygophyllum qatarense*, *Limonium axillare, Helianthemum lippii, Andrachne telephioides, Teucrium polium, Scrophularia deserti, Fagonia* species and solitary young date palms (*Phoenix dactylifera*).

Plant growth on exposed intervening rocky or stony slopes between *wadis* and on the rim rock itself is sparse, mainly comprising desert thorn (*Lycium shawii*) and stunted *Zygophyllum qatarense* with often a space of several metres between each shrub. *Hammada* species and *Salsola imbricata* can be found where there are wind-blown sand deposits on the stony tumuli of west and north-west backslopes. Ancient tumuli occupy much of the west and north backslopes but these were constructed from the existing stony landscape and in fact enhance plant life by creating favourable habitats with rich fine soil deposits in hollows between the mounds.

Run-off water and rich soil deposits favouring growth of annuals and ephemerals accumulate at the foot of backslopes. Species found in such areas in the north and west include:

Malva parviflora	*Arnebia hispidissima*
Filago species	*Aizoon canariense*
Reichardia tingitana	*Mesembryanthemum nodiflorum*
Astragalus spp.	*Trigonella* spp.
Launaea cassiniana	*Anastatica hierochuntica*
	Lotus spp.

and perennials *Francoeuria crispa*, *Eremopogon foveolatus*, *Heliotropium kotschyi* and *Cassia italica*.

The north-east, east and south-east backslopes are largely inhabited, polluted or disturbed. Species occurring on the south-east backslope include *Calligonum polygonoides* ssp. *comosum*, *Eremopogon foveolatus*, *Helianthemum lippii*, *Zygophyllum simplex*, *Heliotropium* sp., *Farsetia heliophila* and *Monsonia nivea*, but the natural features of this whole area have, in recent years, been lost to the quest for backfill and aggregates for local construction industry.

Fagonia spp. are a prominent feature of the stony southern backslope, associated with *Lycium shawii*, *Limonium axillare* and small tussocks of *Stipagrostis socotrana*. Stands of *Pennisetum divisum* and *Cyperus conglomeratus* occur in sandy runnels and *Zygophyllum qatarense* occupies low-lying saline sand.

Jebel Dukhan – north-west slope

The Jebel ridge supports a surprising amount of vegetation. Rocks trap soil and moisture and provide shade, rare in a desert environment. Many plants common to stony desert areas are likely to be seen on the rocky slopes, including *Herniaria hemistemon* and *Andrachne telephioides*, attaining considerable proportions in shady habitats. Particular to the ridge, although occurring elsewhere, are *Ochradenus baccatus*, *Teucrium polium*, *Glossonema varians*, *Erodium glaucophyllum*, *Helianthemum kahiricum*, *Scrophularia deserti*, *Fagonia indica*, *Tetrapogon villosus*, *Chrysopogon* species, *Ifloga spicata*, *Arnebia decumbens* and *Aizoon canariense*. *Ephedra foliata* and *Aerva javanica* are the only species peculiar to this area.

The central depression
Desert soil mainly comprises products from the weathering of rock but, despite its low organic content, supports much vegetation, providing moisture is present.

27

PLANT HABITATS AND ASSOCIATIONS

Three types of habitat occur in the central depression:
1) **Stony gravelly sand** with sparse plant cover, interspersed by shallow depressions with more vegetation where water and fine soil particles accumulate.

Zygophyllum qatarense in central depression

Most distinctive vegetative feature of this area is the low rounded shrub, *Zygophyllum qatarense*, Bahrain's most common and widespread plant. Scattered tussocks of silvery-plumed grass, *Stipagrostis plumosa*, are also a special characteristic of the stony plains. *Cistanche tubulosa* grows by *Zygophyllum qatarense* after rain.

Desert grasses in central depression

Stands of perennial grasses *Eremopogon foveolatus*, *Cymbopogon* species, *Sporobolus arabicus* and *Hyparrhenia hirta*, and annual grass *Stipa capensis* will be observed in shallow depressions where water accumulates.

Plants in depressions receiving run-off from the Jebel ridge, mainly on its east and south sides, include perennials:

Helianthemum lippii

Fagonia spp. *Teucrium polium*

Andrachne telephioides *Erodium glaucophyllum* (locally in the east)

Herniaria hemistemon *Ochradenus baccatus* (locally in the east)

Launaea nudicaulis *Heliotropium kotschyi*

Atractylis flava *Pulicaria gnaphalodes*

Glossonema varians *Convolvulus* sp.

There is dense ephemeral growth with plant cover in these depressions becoming almost closed after rain. Annuals and ephemerals include:

Asphodelus fistulosus *Arnebia hispidissima*

Senecio sp. *Filago* sp.

Oligomeris linifolia *Malva parviflora*

Zygophyllum simplex *Trigonella stellata*

Growth of annuals in *wadi* after rain

East rim rock and *Heliotropium-Taverniera aegyptiaca* community

2) **Wind-blown sand** piles against the rim rock in the south-west and south-east central depression and forms a sand sheet south of the Jebel ridge. *Leptadenia pyrotechnica* grows in the south-west but not in the south-east where smaller shrubs, *Calligonum polygonoides* and *Taverniera aegyptiaca* appear. A *Heliotropium ramosissimum – Panicum turgidum* association occurs in the sand sheet with associates *Cyperus conglomeratus*, *Pennisetum divisum*, *Polycarpaea repens*, *Monsonia nivea*, *Fagonia* spp. and, here and there, small individual date palms (*Phoenix dactylifera*). *Aeluropus lagopoides* grows in saline sand. A remarkable feature dominating the south-east central depression landscape is the 'Tree of Life', an ancient solitary *Prosopis juliflora*.

'Tree of Life' (*Prosopis juliflora*) and *Zygophyllum qatarense-Heliotropium* community in central depression

3) **Sabkha** in the low-lying southern central depression supports just *Zygophyllum qatarense* and a few stunted *Tamarix arabica*.

The central depression north and west of Awali is much disturbed by human activity and the east side has rubbish dumps, factory, rock-crushing plant and quarry. Pipelines and small roads leading to oil and gas installations criss-cross most of the central depression, but pipelines provide plants with shade and moisture in the form of condensation; water runs off road surfaces and accumulates underneath, promoting plant growth along roadsides, and roads at least keep motor traffic from destroying vegetation and habitats. Since four-wheel drive vehicles became popular and common, perennial vegetation has been severely taxed in many places; such disturbance and loss of plant cover aggravates erosion; conversely, wheel-ruts retain moisture and sustain ephemeral plant growth.

On a small island such as Bahrain it is conceivable that, as the population expands, much encroachment by man upon natural areas will occur; especially since all of the terrain is accessible. Nonetheless it should be possible, provided pollution and use of natural resources are strictly controlled, to protect the ecology and preserve the flora of Bahrain.

II

Photographs of Selected Species

SELECTED SPECIES

Calligonum polygonoides

Cynomorium coccineum Desert Thumb

Reichardia species

Sesuvium verrucosum

Dipcadi erythraeum

SELECTED SPECIES

Avicennia marina White Mangrove

Calotropis procera   *Osher*   Apple of Sodom

Taverniera aegyptiaca

SELECTED SPECIES

Halopeplis perfoliata   Khurraiz
'Glass Beads'

Prosopis juliflora pods

Salsola imbricata fruiting

Cassia italica

SELECTED SPECIES

Tetrapogon villosus

Cistanche tubulosa Desert Hyacinth

III

Identification Key Charts

based on the general appearance of plants, with flower
structure and colour in herbs and leaf type in shrubs.
To use the key:
a) Check type of plant e.g. whether shrub or herb
b) If a shrub check:
      1) Whether spinous or not
      2) Whether or not leaves are present or particularly small
      3) If leaves are succulent or flat
      4) Flower colour and formation
      5) Other characteristics of plant
   If a herb check:
      1) Colour and structure of flower
      2) Leaf formation and shape
      3) Other characteristics e.g. habit of plant or kind of fruit
c) Turn to given page number

Species Descriptions
and Illustrations

Plants described in order based on the systems of
A. Takhtajan and A. Cronquist.
Except where an alternative arrangement is suitable,
e.g. Chenopodiaceae and Gramineae (Grasses), genera
and species have been placed in alphabetical order.
✳ Plant not illustrated

1. Herbs FLOWERS WITH PETALS

COLOUR OF FLOWER	FIVE-PETALLED	FOUR-PETALLED	COMPOSITE	LABIATE	PAPILIONATE	OTHER
GREEN	Flr. green and white, small; leaves oval; capsule green **120**					Sepals 5, green and white; leaves oval; capsule green **120** Sepals 5, green; leaves trifoliate; capsule yellow **152**
WHITE	Stems orange, threadlike, leafless **184** Flr. minute; sepals with lateral awns; petals shorter than sepals **63** Flr. very small; sepals longer than petals; leaves linear, fleshy, whorled **64** sepals longer than petals; leaves linear-filiform **67** Calyx tubular; leaves hairy, oblong **67** Flr. bell-shaped, scented; leaves smooth, oblong; pods narrow, long, paired **160** Flr. minute, tubular; leaves blue-green, spathulate **175** Flr. with epicalyx; leaves palmate-lobed **116**	Pl. prostrate; flr. small; stems curling round frt. **99**	Pl. shrubby or not; flr. blue-tinted; leaves dark green **202** Flr. c7.5mm, rays strap-shaped; no pappus; leaves dark green **206** Pl. thistle-like; head globose, florets cream-white; leaves spinous **205** Petals pink-tipped; leaves succulent, swollen **55** Leaves succulent, cylindrical curving; frt. a capsule with triangular flaps **55**	Stems and leaves pale grey with felt-like hairs; flrs. minute, in heads **201** Stems 4-sided; flrs. minute with blue spots in throat **198**	Flrs. minute, in racemes; leaves trifoliate; pods very small **135** Flrs. mauvish; leaves pinnate; pods curved with red blotches **128** Flrs. mauvish; leaves pinnate; pods curved **128**	Flrs. with 6 dark-veined petals; leaves linear **229** Pl. mat-like; flr. fleshy, 5-partite, star-shaped; leaves thick, broad, hairy **52** Pl. erect; flr. 5-partite, star-shaped; leaves long, succulent **52** Staminodes filiform, petal-like, pink tipped; leaves succulent, swollen **55** Staminodes filiform, petal-like; leaves succulent, narrow, terete, curving; frt. capsule with 5 triangular flaps **55**
PINK	Flrs. paniceled, small, papery; leaves spathulate-oblong, rosetted at base **95** Flrs. small, pale, funnel-shaped, in clusters; stamens prominent; leaves minute, ovate **183** Flrs. funnel-shaped; leaves sagittate **180**	Flr. minute; pods linear, c1cm long **103**	Heads small, clustered; leaves broad; also shrub **218**		Flrs. with red veins; leaflets in 5's; pods short **132** Leaflets in 5's; pods linear **132** Pods small, ovoid; leaves trifoliate **136**	

continued overleaf

YELLOW	Pl. sticky, with bristles; corolla irregular; leaves heart-shaped; frt. pods **108**	Stems short, thick; heads large, bright, with or without dark centre; florets strap-shaped; involucre scales pale-margined **221**	Pl. without green colouring; flrs. large, waxy, purple-tinged **187**	Leaves pinnate; pods with horseshoe-shaped segments **131**	Flr. with 5 lobes; stems long, trailing, with tendrils; frt. a small round gourd **99**
	Flrs. small; leaves fleshy, cylindrical **156**	Petals dark-veined; pods linear-oblong, long-beaked **100**	Heads large; florets strap-shaped; leaves finely dissected **217**		Leaves trifoliate; pods coiled into spinous spheres **135**
	Leaves fleshy, spathulate **88**	Petals veined; pods linear, short-beaked **103**	Florets strap-shaped; leaves dentate; no stem leaves **217**		Leaves trifoliate; pods stellate clusters **139**
	Flrs. tubular; leaves, stems, calyx bristly-hairy **171**	Flr. bright yellow; pods drooping, beak very short **100**	Florets strap-shaped; leaves dentate; stem leaves small **217**		Leaves 5-foliate; pods linear **132**
	Leaves large, soft-hairy, crinkle-margined; frt. ovoid, spiny **163**	Flr. pale; pod terete, beaked **100**	Heads large; florets strap-shaped; involucral bracts in 1 row **225**		Flrs. minute, in racemes; leaves trifoliate; pods minute **135**
	Flrs. minute; leaves lobed, woolly; frt. round, spiny **124**	Flr. small, pale; pods long, narrow, held close to stem **104**	Heads large; florets strap-shaped; leaves with rounded auricles **225**		
	Flrs. minute; leaves crenate-margined **119**		Heads large; florets strap-shaped; leaves lobed, with pointed auricles **225**		
	Stems long, trailing, with tendrils; frt. a small round gourd **99**		Leaves spinous; continuing down stem **222**		
			Heads conical; leaves finely dissected **218**		
			Heads globe-shaped, woolly; florets minute **225**		

Flrs. funnel-shaped; leaves oblong-elliptical	**180–183**
Sepals longer than petals; leaves linear	**66**
Pl. mat-like or low-spreading; flrs. minute; leaves minute	**112**
Leaves lacy; frts. long-beaked	**148**
Leaves grey, dentate; frts. long-beaked	**148**

1. Herbs FLOWERS WITH PETALS *continued*

COLOUR OF FLOWER	FIVE-PETALLED	FOUR-PETALLED	COMPOSITE	LABIATE	PAPILIONATE	OTHER
YELLOW *continued*			Heads small, inconspicuous; leaves linear; seed-head spinous **214**			
			Heads with ray and disc florets; rays strap-shaped, disc fl. tubular; leaves fleshy, dissected into few lobes **222**			
PINKISH-MAUVE/ MAGENTA	Leaves large, flat, lobed; frt. beaked; seed with long plume **147**	Flrs. pale; leaves fleshy; lower lobed, upper linear; pods broad, with silvery central partition **104**			Pods ovoid **136**	Sepals 5, with petal-like coloured linings; leaves fleshy, spathulate **56**
	Calyx tubular; leaves smooth, lanceolate **167**	Leaves pinnatifid; pods conical, beaked **103**				
	Flr. tubular; leaves oval, ciliate-margined **179**					
	Flrs. small, papery, panicled; leaves spathulate, rosetted at base **95**					
	Stems fleshy; leaves fleshy, spathulate **56**					
ORANGE/ APRICOT		Pl. creeping along ground; petals pointed; leaves fleshy **88**	Heads with strap-shaped rays and tubular disc florets; fruiting head round, flattened; seeds semicircular **206**			
DARK RED				Pl. with shrubby base; leaves lobed **190**		
BLUE/ PALE MAUVE	Pl. close to ground, hairy; flr. 1mm or less **172**			Pl. without green colouring; corolla tube white, lobes blue **188**	Leaves ending in tendrils **139**	
				Pl. without green colouring; corolla violet **188**	Flrs. whitish; leaves pinnate; pods curving, with red blotches **128**	
					Flrs. whitish; leaves pinnate; pods curving, surface corrugated **128**	

BROWN		Flrs. whitish; leaves pinnate; pods slightly curved **128**		Flrs. bell-shaped, in a raceme; leaves linear **227**

2. Herbs MINUTE CLUSTERED FLOWERS WITH OR WITHOUT PETALS

IDENTIFICATION KEY

COLOUR OF FLOWER	CLUSTERS	HEADS	SPIKES & SPIKELETS	RACEMES	UMBELS
GREEN	Flrs. in wool; stems red; leaves blue-green, fleshy, linear **75**	Heads round, spiny; flrs. without petals; leaves fleshy, linear **64**	**SPIKES**	Leaves large, ovate-triangular; frt. with membranous pink-veined wings **92**	
	Leaves flat, large, ovate, dentate **76**	Flrs. in silvery bracts; leaves minute, oblong **63**	Flrs. clustered; leaves rhomboidal **60**		
	Leaves large, flat, oblong-ovate **60**		Spikes short; flrs. dense; stamens prominent; leaves rosetted at base **189**		
	Perianths spinous; leaves flat, large, ovate **92**		Aquatic plants **226**		
	Pl. mat-like or among rocks; leaves minute, oval **63**		**SPIKELETS**		
	Flrs. in a cup; ovary/capsule on a stalk **123**		Sedges **230–235**		
	Aquatic plants **226**		Grasses—Desert **237–241**		
	Marine plants **226**		Grasses—Sabkha **242**		
			Grasses—Swamp **243–245**		
			Grasses—Irrigated land **246–251**		
			Marine plants **226**		
WHITE	Stems orange, threadlike, leafless **184**	Stems orange, threadlike, leafless **184**		Leaves linear; capsules salmon-pink **112**	Leaves divided into broad lobes **156**
	Flrs. in a cup; ovary/capsule on a stalk **123**			Leaves lobed **112**	
				Leaves large, ovate-triangular; frt. with membranous pink-veined wings **92**	

continued overleaf

2. Herbs MINUTE CLUSTERED FLOWERS WITH OR WITHOUT PETALS *continued*

COLOUR OF FLOWER	CLUSTERS	HEADS	SPIKES & SPIKELETS	RACEMES	UMBELS
YELLOW		Heads in clusters; leaves prominently 3-nerved **209** Pl. prostrate or procumbent, greyish, woolly; heads minute, woolly, in clusters **209**	SPIKES Flrs. between needle-like leaves **214**		Leaves aromatic, divided into filiform segments **156**
PINKISH-MAUVE		Pl. rooting at nodes; heads ovoid, bracteate; **202**			
RED			Pl. without green colouring; spike fleshy, thick, cylindrical **144**		
BROWN	Leaves rigid, erect, cylindrical, sharp **230**		Spike large, cylindrical, velvety; leaves long, linear **256** SPIKELETS Sedges **230-235**		

3. Shrubs and Trees SPINOUS

Unless otherwise described plants in this section are all shrubs

COLOUR OF FLOWER	SUCCULENT-LEAVED	FLAT-LEAVED	LEAVES ABSENT, MINUTE OR LINEAR
GREEN	Stems fleshy; leaves ending in long spine; yellow stamens conspicuous 76		
WHITE		Flrs. large, 4-petalled, irregular; leaves orbicular; frt. pear-shaped 107	
PINK		Pl. compact; flrs. 5-petalled, mauvish; leaves oval 151-2	
YELLOW		Flrs. minute, whitish, in catkins; leaves bipinnate; pods purplish-black, swollen 140	
		Tree with pendulous branches; flrs. minute, whitish, in catkins; leaves bipinnate; pods long, flat 143	
		Tree or shrub; leaves bipinnate; flrs. minute, whitish, in globular heads; pods long, flat, twisted 140	
		Flrs. greenish, 5-petalled, fleshy; leaves orbicular; frt. round, fleshy, with hard seed 159	
PINKISH-MAUVE/ MAGENTA		Flrs. papilionate; spines green, fleshy; leaves small, oval 127	Flrs. papilionate; spines green, fleshy 127
BLUE/ PALE MAUVE		Flrs. tubular; leaves small, oblong-spathulate; frt. a red berry 193	Flrs. tubular; frt. a red berry 193

4. Shrubs and Trees WITHOUT SPINES

COLOUR OF FLOWER	SUCCULENT-LEAVED		FLAT-LEAVED		LEAVES ABSENT, MINUTE OR LINEAR	
GREEN	Pl. compact; stems fleshy; leaves opp. cylindrical; frt. with pink or white wings	71	Flrs. bell-shaped; leaves large; frt.red, in woolly calyx	194	Stems thick, succulent, jointed; flrs. and frt.in stems	83
	Flrs. fleshy, clustered or single; leaves linear-cylindrical, yellow-green	80	Flrs. fleshy, minute, in clusters; leaves grey, triangular, crinkled	72	Stems slender, succulent, jointed; flrs. in joints; frt. with whitish or pink wings	79
	Stems pale grey, woody; leaves cylindrical, swollen at tip; frt. with minute wings	87	Flr. without petals; sepals 5; capsule green	120	Flrs. minute, greyish, woolly, clustered in spikes; frt. with pink or white wings	79
	Flrs. fleshy, clustered; leaves oblong, greyish; fruiting stems and frt. blackish	80			Flrs. minute, fleshy, clustered, with fishy odour; frt. with whitish wings	75
					Stems blue-green, succulent, jointed; flr.-spikes decussate	84
WHITE	Pl. compact; flr. with 5 petals; leaves almost spherical	155	Pl. compact, with bristly hairs; flrs. minute, tubular, cymose	175-6	Flrs. 5-petalled; frt. red, hairy	91-92
	Pl. compact; calyx spinous; petals 5; leaves oblong-cylindrical, greyish	68	Pl. compact, whitish; flrs. minute, in white fleecy spikes	59		
			Pl. compact; flrs. tubular with limb and yellow centre; leaves small, hairy, elliptical	172		
			Flrs. composite, tinged blue; leaves dark green	202		
			Pl. tall, tree-like; flrs. in large panicles, showy; leaves tough, pinnate; frt. fleshy with hard seed	252		
			Shrub or tree with milky sap; flrs. 5 petals, pink-purple-tipped; frt. large, green, globose	163		
PINK	Pl. compact; flr.-spikes pink, fleshy; leaves perfoliate, almost spherical	84	Flr. papilionate, veined; leaves oval; pods flat with red bristles	136	Flrs. tubular with triangular petal-tips; flrs. in papery toothed sheaths	168
			Flr. papilionate, with red veins; leaves hairy, small, in 5's; pods short, rounded	132	Pl. tall, tree-like or not; flrs. in spikes; leaves clasping	115

Colour	Description	Page
YELLOW	Flrs. composite; heads clustered	218
	Pl. very small; flrs. 5-petalled; leaves elliptical-oblong	96
	Flrs. large, 4-petalled, irregular; leaves pinnate; pods broad, flat	124
	Flrs. composite; heads globose; stems whitish; leaves small, dentate	221
	Flrs. composite; dull yellow; leaves woolly, very aromatic	213
	Flrs. composite, discoid; no rays; leaves wavy, clasping	210
	Flrs. composite, discoid, with ray florets; leaves wavy, clasping	210
	Pl. tall; stems green, usually leafless; flrs. greenish, fleshy, 5-petalled; frt. pod-like	164
	Flrs. minute, without petals, in spikes; frt. white, globose; leaves linear	111
PINKISH-MAUVE/MAGENTA	Pl. compact; flrs. fleshy, purplish; leaves oblong-linear, grey-purple-red	87
ORANGE/APRICOT	Leaves leathery, white beneath; stems whitish; habitat muddy shore/marsh	197
DARK RED	Pl. compact; flr. 4-petalled; leaves, stems, pods grey	100
BROWN	Flrs. cone-like; stems greenish, flexuous; leaves scale-like	51

EPHEDRACEAE

IA

Ephedra foliata

IB

Fruit

IC

Female flowers

GYMNOSPERMS

EPHEDRACEAE

Woody shrubs with many slender, erect or sprawling, greenish branches. Leaves opposite, reduced to minute scales. Monoecious plants, with inflorescences of cones, which are solitary or clustered.

Ephedra foliata Boiss. ex C.A. Mey.   *I*

An unusual plant, rare on Bahrain. Only two specimens have been recorded, both in a rocky S-N gully in the centre of the Jebel at c 100m. The shrub may grow to 1.5m high, but here its thick grey main stem is hidden as it climbs up from deep beneath rocks, and just a few branches protrude from a crevice; these are spindly, flexible and grey-green in colour. The male cones are pale brown, 6mm long, at tips and nodes of branches, usually in threes; the female cones are whitish globose structures enclosed in bracts, solitary or in pairs, and ripen into hard fruits 4 – 5mm long, each comprising 2 – 3 hard blackish seeds encased in a brown papery envelope.

Flowers February – April.

First recorded Bahrain M.A. 1985.

Certain plants of this genus yield 'ephedrine', used in the treatment of colds, asthma and hay fever.

ANGIOSPERMS

MAGNOLIOPSIDA (Dicotyledons)

AIZOACEAE (Carpetweed Family)

Fleshy papillose annual herbs with simple, opposite or alternate
leaves. The flowers have 5 sepals and lack petals. Fruit a
dehiscent capsule.

2 *Aizoon canariense* L.   Ed. Herb. 152, 298

This attractive ground plant appears after even minimal rainfall
on compact fine silty soils in all desert areas including the Jebel.
Its branches spread, or zig-zag, from the base tight to the ground
forming neat, satisfying star shapes up to 30cm wide. Its bright
green leaves are alternate, obovate, fleshy, softly hairy and
glistening. Flowers single, sessile, 4mm across, without petals;
the triangular tips of the fleshy calyx forming a 5-pointed star
shape, whitish-green with a yellow centre. Tiny seeds form in a
flattened 5-sided capsule and the whole plant turns woody as it
matures.
   Flowers March – May.
   The leaves are edible and may be used in salads. Also grazed by
camels.
   Recorded Hawar island group C.C. 1983.

3 *Aizoon hispanicum* L.

A small bright green erect succulent with long fleshy leaves in
pairs. Its attractive white flowers are star-shaped, c 12mm across
and borne singly in leaf axils or at stem tips.
   Flowers January – March.
   Recorded Hawar island group C.C. 1983 and R.G. Bahrain
1950.

2A

Aizoon canariense

3

Aizoon hispanicum

2B

Aizoon canariense

4

Mesembryanthemum forskahlei

5ᴬ

5ᴮ

▲

◄ *Mesembryanthemum nodiflorum*

Mesembryanthemum forskahlei Hochst.   Ed. Herb. 58, 59   **4**

This small succulent herb is not common and, though it will grow
in sandy desert areas, seems to prefer less harsh conditions near
cultivation or villages. Of decumbent habit, it reaches a height of
15cm and has extremely fleshy glistening leaves and branches.
Each flower has a much swollen calyx diverging into conical
leaf-like lobes, between which is a daisy-like centre 12mm across,
composed of many fragile white pink-tipped filaments
surrounding a cluster of yellow stamens.
   Flowers January – April.

Mesembryanthemum nodiflorum L.   Ed. Herb. 60   **5**

A succulent plant very common after good rainfall on fine sandy
soils with silty deposits, especially near villages. Its many tough,
though slender, decumbent stems grow to a height of 20cm and
spread out to form large clumps. The dark green leaves glisten
with papillae; they are opposite, 10 – 15mm long, terete, curving
upwards. In dry conditions leaves may be red. Flowers solitary,
10mm wide, with many white petal-like staminodes around a
centre of yellow stamens; they open to the sun then close just after
midday. Tiny seeds ripen in a capsule closed by five triangular
flaps which split open from the apex immediately upon contact
with water.
   Flowers April – May.

6   *Sesuvium verrucosum* Raf.   Ed. Herb. 12, 273/4, 310/11

Spreads of this sturdy annual succulent are a familiar sight along roads, around habitations and fields and in waste places, in the northern areas of the island. Its decumbent fleshy green, or reddish, stems reach a height of 30cm and spread about covering wide areas of ground. Leaves opposite, bright to bluish-green, fleshy, spathulate or oblong-obovate, with surface deposits of salts. Flowers in leaf axils, singly or in twos or threes. They have no petals, but the 5 sepals are bright mauvish-pink or magenta-coloured on the inside; these colourful linings overlap the outer green part of the sepals and resemble 5 pointed petals when the flower opens. The stamens also are mauvish-pink. Each green sepal ends in a small green horn. Flowers 10mm across; only open in direct sunlight. Many hard shiny minute blackish seeds disperse from an open capsule*.

Flowers February onwards. Plants die back in winter.
A ruderal plant, providing useful ground cover in many localities, but possibly also a tiresome weed in others as it speedily colonises untended gardens and fields.
Recorded Hawar island group C.C. 1983.

*Illustration p.34

6A   *Sesuvium verrucosum* with *Salsola baryosma*

6B   *Sesuvium verrucosum*

6C   *Sesuvium verrucosum*

7*A*

Aerva javanica

7*C*   *Aerva javanica* Ripening fruit

7*B*   *Aerva javanica* Flowers

AMARANTHACEAE (Amaranth Family)

Herbs or shrubs with simple alternate leaves and minute flowers clustered on spikes or in axils. Fruit has one seed.

Aerva javanica (Burm.f.) Juss.   Ed. Herb. 171, 240   **7**

A small shrub found in sandy sediment between rocks and in gullies on west and south-west facing slopes of the Jebel. It has pale stiff erect stems, reaching a height of 50cm, with old greyish-white wood at its base. The pale green leaves, 20 – 40mm long, have a covering of matted hairs; upper surface with a grainy appearance. Flowers creamy-white, with 5 woolly sepals, clustered on spikes along upper stems; buds and flower-centres pinkish. Fruits immersed in silky white fleece; the whole plant appearing white at the fruiting stage. Fruits globose, single-seeded*.

    Flowers January – May.

    Arabic name: *'Tirf'* or *'Ra'*.

    In other countries flower-heads used formerly for stuffing pillows and saddles.

*p.19

AMARANTHACEAE

8   *Amaranthus graecizans* L.   Ed. Herb. 86, 124

An annual green herb, growing to a height of 50cm, with few
sturdy ascending stems from the base of the main stem. Stems
pale green; leaves deep green, 40mm long, oblong to ovate,
blunt-tipped, tapering towards the base, petioled. Flowers green,
2mm long, borne in dense clusters in leaf axils along each stem.
Fruit a green capsule containing one minute black shiny seed.
   Flowers April.
   Arabic name: *'Khubbayz'*.
   A common weed of roadsides, gardens and fields. Needs high
   water-table or irrigation.

9   *Amaranthus viridis* L.   Ed. Herb. 116

Also an annual weed, up to 50cm high, with deep green ovate to
rhomboidal leaves on long petioles. Inflorescence of one terminal
spike up to 8cm long and lesser axillary spikes; flowers green,
clustered, spikes narrow. Fruit a one-seeded capsule.
   Flowers April – June.

8A

Amaranthus graecizans

8B   *Amaranthus graecizans*

9   *Amaranthus viridis*

61

IOB

Herniaria hemistemon ▶

▼

IOA

IIB

▲

◀ *Paronychia arabica*

IIA

CARYOPHYLLACEAE (Pink Family)

Herbs or subshrubs with simple, opposite or apparently whorled leaves. Flowers are in terminal or axillary cymes or solitary; sepals usually 5; petals 5, sometimes shorter than sepals or absent. Fruit single or many-seeded.

Herniaria hemistemon J. Gay Ed. Herb. 35, 45   *IO*

A perennial prostrate mat-like little plant, common in silty depressions and compact desert soils in the central depression and backslope areas; also growing vigorously in shady crevices on the Jebel, protruding fern-like from between rocks. It has elliptical leaves, only 5 – 7mm long and numerous clusters of minute green flowers. Minute fruits, less than 1mm long contain a single seed within a membranous chamber.
    Flowers January – May.

Herniaria hirsuta L.   *

A herb similar to H. hemistemon, but usually annual and with longer narrower leaves.   R.A.K. & K.J.K.

Loeflingia hispanica L.   *

Small annual herb with minute flowers in terminal and axillary cymes. Sepals with lateral awns. Petals white, shorter than sepals.   R.G. 1950.

Paronychia arabica (L.) DC. Ed. Herb. 144   *II*

Prostrate mat-like annual, seen in compact gravelly sand near cultivation east of Dumistan. Characterised by small silvery heads composed of scarious bracts enveloping minute flowers. Leaves minute, oblong, 5 – 7mm long. Flower-heads dispersed along thin straggling stems; bracts 3 – 5mm long, longer than sepals. Fruit 1-seeded.
    Flowers April, or after rain.

I2   *Polycarpaea repens* (Forssk.) Asch. & Schweinf.   Ed. Herb. 50, 162

Semi-prostrate perennial, often with just a few cm of the plant appearing above the loose sand in which it grows. Seen in all areas of blown sand; including the south-east quarter of the central depression and small dunes east of Jazayir. Lower stems grey, woody; upper stems spindly, green. Leaves slightly fleshy, 3 – 6mm long, clustered at nodes. Flowers minute, 1 – 2mm long with green sepals longer than the white petals. Seeds in a capsule.

    Flowers March – April.

    Associated with *Monsonia nivea* and *Moltkiopsis ciliata*.

*   *Polycarpaea spicata* Wight & Arn.

                                                   R.A.K. & K.J.K.

*   *Polycarpon arabicum* Boiss.

                                                 R.G. 1950.

I3   *Sclerocephalus arabicus* Boiss.   Ed. Herb. 2, 169, 196

An annual herb requiring little moisture, growing in stony sand in a *wadi* east of Hamad Town, also in sandy gullies on the western slopes of the Jebel. It is only 3 – 4cm high, and sometimes 10 – 12cm wide though usually less. Leaves terete, fleshy, 10 – 20mm long. Minute flowers among green spines in rounded heads 8mm across; the spiny heads become hard as the fruits mature; fruit 1-seeded, indehiscent.

    Flowers February – May.

12B

12A

▲ *Polycarpaea repens* ▶

13B

Sclerocephalus arabicus ▲ ▶

13A

65

14 *Spergularia bocconii* (Scheele) Asch. & Graebn.   Ed. Herb. 117, 143

A delicate green herb, 10 – 15cm high, common among grasses and other weeds along sides of irrigation ditches. Leaves in opposite pairs or whorls, linear, terete. Flowers with five pink petals, 3mm long. Many dark grey minute seeds in a capsule.
Flowers March – May.

14A

Spergularia bocconii

14B

Silene villosa Forssk.   ✳
An uncommon herb of sandy soils on the western backslopes.
Leaves green, long, narrow with rounded apex. Calyx long,
tubular, with five teeth; petals white.   R.G. 1950. D.B. 1979/81.

Spergula fallax (Lowe) E.H.L. Krause   ✳
   Flowers white.   R.G. 1950.

Spergularia diandra (Guss.) Heldr. & Sart.   ✳
                                        R.A.K. & K.J.K.

Spergularia marina (L.) Griseb.   ✳
                                        R.A.K. & K.J.K.

15 *Sphaerocoma aucheri* Boiss. Ed. Herb. 62, 77, 220

This low sprawling grey-branched shrub is uncommon; recorded on reclaimed land by the Tubli Bay road. Height up to 30cm. Leaves fleshy, dark green, sometimes greyish, about 5mm long. Flowers in clusters of five, white, 5-petalled with 5 spiked sepals. Fruits spiky, brownish-green, single-seeded, indehiscent.

Flowers December – January.

15A *Sphaerocoma aucheri*

15B

Sphaerocoma aucheri Leaves and flower-buds

15D

15C   *Sphaerocoma aucheri* Flowers

Sphaerocoma aucheri Fruit

16A

Anabasis setifera

16D

16B   *Anabasis setifera* Flowers

With exudation from insects

16C

Anabasis setifera Fruit

CHENOPODIACEAE
(Goosefoot, Glasswort Family)

Shrubs or herbs with simple, opposite or alternate leaves
sometimes reduced to scales; most with succulent parts. Flowers
minute, green, without petals; perianth comprising usually 5
sepal-like parts. Fruit 1-seeded.

Anabasis setifera Moq.   Ed. Herb. 94/5, 212, 217, 362   *16*

This bright green succulent shrublet, c 25 – 40cm high, with its
unmistakable stem and leaf formation thrives in gypsic soils in
most areas, in association with *Suaeda vermiculata* or *Zygophyllum
qatarense*. Stems, leaves and flowers fleshy, sometimes tinged
purple; leaves c 5mm long; minute flowers with perianth of five
fleshy parts and yellow stamens in leaf-axils. In flower the plant is
pleasantly scented and attracts many winged insects. At fruiting
stage it is showy, covered with clusters of winged fruits;
fruit-wings papery, parchment-or pink-coloured; seeds minute,
blackish-brown.
  New shoots appear February, flowers October – November,
  fruits late November.
  Vernacular name: '*Sha'ran*'.
  Anabasis seems to be the favourite host of minute scale-like
  insects, that appear to hatch in globules of white sticky foam,
  then emerge to live, attached like limpets, on the plant stems.
  Grazed by camels.
  Recorded Hawar island group C.C. 1983 & 1985.

Anabasis articulata (Forssk.) Moq.   ✳

B.N.H.S. 1987.

*I*7   *Atriplex leucoclada* Boiss.   Ed. Herb. 51/2, 216, 309, 347
Perennial salt-secreting shrub, growing in stony gypsic soils,
often forming thickets with *Suaeda vermiculata*, on
long-abandoned fields north-east of Aali and east of Dumistan;
also found in a large *wadi* east of Hamad Town, and many other
similar localities. The whole shrub has a pale greyish aspect,
except during January and February when it produces
pinkish-red shoots; stems, leaves and flowers are coated with fine
matted wool and salt crystals. Leaves alternate, pale grey-green,
flat, triangular or deltoid with undulate margins, up to 25mm
long. Slender flower-stems bear sparse clusters of pale grey-green
fleshy nodular flowers; male flowers with yellow stamens. Female
flowers develop into flat grey-green fruits, each composed of a
leathery envelope fringed with lobes, containing 1 minute black
seed*.
   Flowers September.
   English name: 'Orache'.
   Eaten by sheep and camels. *Atriplex* species are a good source
   of fodder, with high protein content.

*p.18

17ᴬ

Atriplex leucoclada

17ᴰ

Flowers

Fruit

17ᶜ

17ᴮ

Atriplex leucoclada

18A
Bassia eriophora

19A

19C

19B

◀ *Salsola baryosma* ▶

Fruit

Bassia eriophora (Schrad.) Asch.   Ed. Herb. 271   *18*

Small annual herb, 15cm high, with few branches. The plant
appears soft and woolly, as stems leaves and flowers have long
white silky hairs. Stems pinky-red; leaves bluish-green; some
leaves 20 – 30mm x 2mm and swollen, but most flat, 5 – 15mm
long.
  Flowers March – April.
  Grows near irrigated areas, on open ground and by roads.

Salsola baryosma (Roem. & Schult.) Dandy   Ed. Herb. 56/7,
82/3, 114, 227   *19*

A shrub which grows profusely around the borders of fields and
villages. Of untidy tangled habit, with frondy stems ascending to
a height of 1m; stems pale, whitish or yellowish, with bright
blue-green buds in small clusters along their length. In moist
places young branches tend to be reddish, soft and fern-like. The
tiny fleshy leaves are woolly. Flowers bright green, fleshy,
minute, 2mm long, densely clustered on short flower-stems,
bisexual, with yellow stamens protruding. Fruiting perianths
5-partite, wings silvery, sometimes pink-tinged; fruit 1-seeded*.
  New growth February, flowers April – October, fruits October
  – December.
  Vernacular name: '*Hamd*'.
  The juice of plants in dry habitats reeks of rotting fish.

*p.18

20   *Chenopodium murale* L.   Ed. Herb. 61
Annual green weed of gardens and inhabited areas. Stems 20cm
or more high, green, sometimes reddish; leaves on long petioles,
flat, broad, triangular with dentate margins, 40mm long. Flowers
minute, green, in clusters. Seeds minute, black.
   Flowers April.

*   *Chenopodium glaucum* L.
Leaves narrower than *C. murale*, green above, white underneath.
                                                        R.G. 1950.

21   *Cornulaca monacantha* Del.   Ed. Herb. 53/4
A spiny shrub with fleshy stems up to 60cm high, only seen in
northern areas, north-west of Sar, east of Dumistan and on
reclaimed land in Umm Al Hassam, in sandy soil. Stems and
leaves greyish blue-green. Each leaf tapers to a long spine.
Flowers hidden, but yellow stamens conspicuous. Fruit spinous*.
   Flowers October – November.
   Arabic name: '*Had*'.

*   *Cornulaca leucacantha* Charif & Aellen
                                                    B.N.H.S. 1987.

*p.19

20

Chenopodium murale

21B

Cornulaca monacantha ▶
▼

21A

Flowering branch

CHENOPODIACEAE

22B Flowering

22C Fruit

◀ *Haloxylon persicum*

22A

23A

Salsola imbricata & *Haloxylon persicum*

Salsola imbricata Flowers **23B**

Haloxylon persicum Boiss.   Ed. Herb. 185, 213   **22**
    =*Hammada salicornica* (Moq.) Iljin

A shrub growing on and around the gravemounds near Sar in dry
stony soil, in association with *Salsola imbricata*. The bushes tend
to be small, due to browsing by camels and goats. New stem
growth slender, green, succulent, jointed and leafless. Flowers
contained in the joints of bright green succulent flower-spikes.
Fruit-wings whitish, occasionally pink, 4mm long. Stems become
woody as fruits mature.
    Flowers August – October, fruits November.
    Arabic name: *'Rimth'*.
    Globules of sticky white foam, nests of scaly insects, seen on
    the flower stems in September.

Salsola imbricata Forssk.   Ed. Herb. 214/15, 339   **23**

A small shrub growing locally on the stony gravemounds.
Branches grey and brittle. Flowers minute, greyish-green,
woolly, with protruding stamens, clustered tightly along short
flower-stems of varying lengths. Fruiting perianth with
parchment-coloured or bright pink wings, 3mm across*.
    Flowers August – October, fruits November.
    Arabic name: *'Hadh'*.

Salsola vermiculata L.   *

    K.V. 1978/79.

*Illustration p.39

24 *Suaeda aegyptiaca* (Hasselq.) Zohary   Ed. Herb. 55, 78, 99,
259,330/31
> =*Schanginia aegyptiaca* (Hasselq.) Aellen

Small succulent-leaved decumbent shrub, height 75cm, in moist
habitats near irrigation, distinguishable by its bright yellow-green
colour; young plants deeper green, turning paler as they flower.
Leaves fleshy, up to 12mm x 3mm, rounded at the tip, curving
upwards. Minute green fleshy flowers clustered near stem tips or
borne singly in leaf axils. Fruit surrounded by the 5 ripened
fleshy flower segments; less than 2mm. long.
> New growth February – March; flowers May onwards.

25 *Suaeda vermiculata* Forssk. ex Gmelin   Ed. Herb. 79, 80, 156,
312

The most common shrub of northern areas, around villages,
farms and waste ground, forming large tangled thickets up to 2m
high. In moist habitats in association with *Salsola baryosma*, and
in dry soil with *Atriplex leucoclada*. Leaves greyish tinged purple,
fleshy, oblong, 5 – 12mm long, slightly curving. Flowers minute,
green or reddish, fleshy, clustered. Seeds and stems bearing fruits
black*.
> Flowers May – October, fruits November – December, new
> shoots February.
> Arabic name: '*Suwaida*'; vernacular name: '*Simayr*' or
> '*Gadgad*'.
> Recorded Hawar island group C.C. 1983 & 1985.

*p.18

24A *Suaeda aegyptiaca* with *S. vermiculata*

24B Flowering ▲
◄ Fruit *Suaeda aegyptiaca*

24C

Suaeda vermiculata ►
▼

Flowers

25B

25A

26A

26C Flower-stem ▲

Arthrocnemum macrostachyum ▶

26B
Flowers

27B Flowering ▲

Arthrocnemum salicornicum ▶

27A

Arthrocnemum macrostachyum (Moric.) Moris & Delponte   **26**
     Ed. Herb. 107, 32, 342, 361

Succulent halophytic plant of saline damp sandy seashores occasionally swamped by high tides, particularly from Ras Tubli to Ras Ikur, between east-coastal villages Askar and Jau, and at Ras Al Barr on small sand dunes adjacent to the beach. Many sprawling procumbent branches sprout from a short woody main stem. Flowering stems held erect, up to 75cm high, robust thick and fleshy, without leaves. Succulent flower spikes, 15 – 30mm long; flowers partly hidden in joints, yellow stamens conspicuous. 6 pyramid-shaped 2.5mm long seeds fitted into a cup inside each joint; seeds pale brownish-grey, fruiting stems pale brown.
     Flowers April – May; fruits July – September.
     Arabic name: '*Shinan*'.
     Recorded Hawar island group C.C. 1983 & 1985.

Arthrocnemum salicornicum (Moric.) Moris & Delponte   Ed.
Herb. 218   **27**

Small erect plant 20 – 40cm high, of the muddy littoral shore around Tubli Bay. Stems red at the base and tip, jointed, succulent, shiny, almost glassy. Flower-spikes short, bright green; flowers in stem joints, with styles and stamens protruding.
     Flowers September – October, also January – February.
     A halophyte that tolerates twice-daily swamping by sea water*.

Salicornia herbacea L.   *****
Recorded at Ras Tubli.   K.V. 1978/79.

*p.18

28 *Halocnemum strobilaceum* (Pall.) M. Bieb.   Ed. Herb. 91, 186, 211, 324, 335

Perennial pale blue-green shrub, 35cm high, with lower stems usually in sand hummocks, widely distributed along the eastern side of the island, in damp salines and coastal *sabkhas*. Profuse untidy woody branches form sizeable clumps. Shoots slender, jointed, fleshy, with fleshy leaves like buds between joints; leaf-buds and flower-spikes arranged in distinctive decussate formation. Flower-spikes 10 – 20mm long, resembling tubercles, with tightly inserted flowers between fleshy bracts; stamens protruding. Fruits wingless; seeds less than 1mm long; each seed in a membranous pocket between shrunken bracts[*1].

Flowers August – November.

Vernacular name: '*Toof*'.

Intensively grazed by camels, also by gazelle on the south-east *sabkha*.

Recorded Hawar island group C.C. 1983 & 1985.

✻   *Halopeplis amplexicaulis*   K.V. 1978/79.

29 *Halopeplis perfoliata* (Forssk.) Bge.   Ed. Herb. 93, 108, 318

A tiny halophytic shrub with spherical perfoliate succulent leaves threaded, like beads, onto the stems. It dominates communities in damp coastal *sabkhas* bordering beaches along the eastern and western shores. Height of main stem c 30cm, with erect lateral branches c 10cm long. Colour of leaves often red, diameter 10mm, length 7mm. Flower-spikes very similar to those of *Halocnemum strobilaceum* but alternate. Flowers red, fleshy, between bracts, in cylindrical spikes up to 30mm long. Plants conspicuously, attractively pink when in flower. Fruit in a membranous pocket between shrunken bracts, contains 1 seed, and is without wings; seed less than 1mm long[*2].

Flowers November – January.

Arabic name: '*Khurraiz*', meaning 'glass beads'.

Recorded Hawar island group C.C. 1983 & 1985.

[*1]. p.18
[*2]. Illustration p.38

28A

28B

28C

Halocnemum strobilaceum

Flower-spikes

29B Flower-spikes

Halopeplis perfoliata

29A

CHENOPODIACEAE

30A

30C

Flowers

Seidlitzia rosmarinus

30B Fruit

31

Suaeda maritima

Seidlitzia rosmarinus (Ehrenb.) Bge.   Ed. Herb. 207, 319, 341, 353   *30*

A 1m high halophytic shrub, sharing the small Ras Al Barr sand dunes with *Arthrocnemum macrostachyum*. Grey woody branches spread laterally from a sturdy central stem up to 3cm in diameter. Leaves green, very fleshy, slightly curved, bulbous-tipped, 4 – 12mm long, often with a cobwebby aspect. Flowering stems also woody, but slender, pale grey, ascending, each with several axillary flower-stalks towards the tip. Flowers pale green, fleshy, minute with prominent yellow stamens; clustered in woolly axils. Fruits globe-shaped, 2.5mm across, with pale green wings of unequal length all less than 1mm long.
   Flowers August – September.
   Arabic name: '*Shinaa*'.
   Dried leaves from these plants and several other chenopod (goosefoot) species are used in soap-making. The leaves act as a water softener and may be substituted for soap.

Suaeda maritima (L.) Dum.   Ed. Herb. 190, 219, 323   *31*

Grey shrublet of the muddy Tubli Bay littoral shoreline and shore of the channel between Sitra and Ikur. Stems c 25cm high, woody at the base; young shoots and leaves succulent but soft, not turgid. Leaves alternate, grey, tinged reddish or purple, semi-terete, 15mm long. Flowers reddish-purple, fleshy, minute; single or in clusters at intervals along upper stem and in axils. Fruit of 1 seed enclosed by the 5 fleshy perianth segments; the whole plant becoming reddish at this stage[*1].
   Flowers October – November, also January.
   Vernacular name: '*Rijla*'.
   This halophyte seems to thrive on sea water. During November the marshy coastline by Sanad becomes transformed – aglow with masses of *Suaeda maritima* in all shades of pink, red and orange[*2].

[*1]. p.18
[*2]. Illustration p.21

PORTULACACEAE (Purslane Family)
Herbs with succulent stems and leaves; leaves simple and
opposite or alternate. Flowers are borne singly or in clusters;
petals 4 – 5. Fruit a capsule with many seeds.

32 *Portulaca oleracea* L.   Ed. Herb. 89, 138
Succulent annual herb with fleshy decumbent stems to c 15cm
high. Stems and leaves smooth, deep green, often purple-tinged.
Leaves fleshy, spathulate, 20mm long. Flowers 5 – 7mm across,
with 5 bright yellow notched petals, open only in the morning.
Tiny black seeds disperse from a capsule.
    Flowers March and through the year.
    Vernacular name: *'Berbir'*.
    Weed of roadsides and gardens, also cultivated for use in salads
    and as a potherb.

33 *Portulaca quadrifida* L.   Ed. Herb. 200
Creeping plant of fields and irrigated areas in the north. It has
fleshy stems and leaves with long white hairs or filaments from
the nodes. Stems and leaves red in dry habitats; leaves lanceolate.
Flowers solitary, with four pale apricot-coloured petals, 5mm
long; open only before noon.
    Flowers April.

32   Portulaca oleracea

33ᴮ

33ᴬ

Portulaca quadrifida

POLYGONACEAE

34ᴬ

Calligonum polygonoides

34ᶜ

34ᴮ

Fruit

90

POLYGONACEAE (Buckwheat Family)

Herbs or shrubs with usually jointed stems and swollen nodes; leaves simple, alternate. Flowers are borne in clusters or racemes; sepals 5 – 6, petals absent. Fruit an achene.

Calligonum polygonoides L.   Ed. Herb. 248, 251   **34**

This shrub with stout gnarled grey stem and many branches appears dead most of the year. It grows in the generous deposits of wind-blown sand along the central depression perimeter and backslopes on the east and west sides of the island. New growth consists of many slender needle-like green stems, characteristically jointed, that bear clusters of pedicelled tiny white sweet-scented flowers, 4mm across. Base of sepals and stamens reddish. Leaves minute and soon shed. Fruits achenes, with bright red fleshy coverings fused into ridges fringed with soft fleshy bristles, 12mm long, resembling lanterns suspended from the branches. When ripe and dry the fruits drop to the sand to be tumbled away by the wind*.

New shoots January, flowers and fruits February – early March.

Arabic name: '*Abal*'.

The bushes may reach a height of 1.5m or more, but the main stems are usually inundated by the soft sand in which they grow, and camels often browse the green shoots. The fruits are edible and freshen the mouth with their tart taste, the pounded and dried leaves are said to be used in a balm for skin ailments, and the wood is sought for camp fires in countries where its growth is more prolific.

*Illustration p.32

Calligonum polygonoides L. subsp. *comosum* (L'Her.) Sosk.   Ed. Herb. 46

Very small bushes, 25cm high, possibly browsed, on the south-eastern backslope south of Dur.

35   *Emex spinosus* (L.) Campd.   Ed. Herb. 158

Annual herb, 10 – 15cm high, glabrous and broad-leaved, growing in fine soils near farms. Also recorded in a *wadi* near the Tree of Life* following heavy rainfall. Leaves large, deep green, ovate, truncate at the base. Flowers minute, green, red-tipped, in clusters at nodes. Spiny hardened perianth remains round fruit; fruit an achene, 3 – 4mm long.

  Flowers in March and April.

  Arabic name: '*Hammaidh*'.

*   *Rumex vesicarius* L.

Glabrous annual herb with large ovate to triangular leaves on long petioles. The flowers, borne along the stem, are small but the fruits are conspicuous, with large pink-veined membranous wings enclosing each seed.

  Recorded on the backslopes and central depression by R.G. 1950.

  A member of the 'Dock' family that is edible, either raw or cooked; also used medicinally as a laxative or tonic.

*p.30

35^A   Emex spinosus

35^B   Emex spinosus

PLUMBAGINACEAE

▲
◀ *Limonium axillare*
▼

36C

36B

PLUMBAGINACEAE (Sea-lavender Family)

Herbs with leaves in basal rosettes; inflorescence a branched 1-sided spike; fruit with 1 seed.

Limonium axillare (Forssk.) O. Kuntze   Ed. Herb. 43a/b, 238   *36*

Perennial salt-secreting plant appearing in all localities, but thriving particularly well in saline gypsic soils between the backslopes and coasts in the north and east. Width of plants varies between 10 – 100cm; height c 30cm when in flower. Bright green leathery leaves, 10 x 50mm, rosetted at the base, usually thickly crusted with salts, becoming greyish in dry conditions. Attractive in flower, producing many showy panicles of pink papery flowers; flowers 2 – 4mm long. Fruit has a single minute ovoid brown seed in a tough membranous sheath*.

New growth January – February; flowers early March until June.
Possibly pollinated by *Adesmia* beetles feeding on nectar in the flowers.
Recorded Hawar island group C.C. 1983 & 1985.

*p.18

CISTACEAE (Rockrose Family)

Shrublets or herbs with simple entire leaves. Inflorescence a
scorpioid cyme; flowers yellow, with 5 sepals and 5 petals. Fruit
an ovoid 3-valved capsule with many seeds.

37   *Helianthemum kahiricum* Del.   Ed. Herb. 172, 358

Tiny perennial shrub with fragile brittle branches, c 25cm high,
growing in sand deposits in rocky gullies, most commonly on the
slopes of the Jebel. Its brilliant yellow flowers, though small,
stand out in contrast to its dark green foliage and shady habitat.
Leaves elliptical-oblong, 5 – 8mm long, margins often rolled,
greyish in dry conditions. Flowers pedicelled, 5-petalled, 5mm
across, along stem-tips. Seeds develop in a capsule which splits
open into three valves to release them*.
    Flowers April – May and October.

38   *Helianthemum lippii* (L.) Dum.-Cours.   Ed. Herb. 64, 130, 150

Similar to *H. kahiricum* but smaller, more compact, c 15cm high.
Leaves sparse, smaller, greyish and with a pronounced
indentation along the midrib; flowers sessile or almost so, closely
grouped along stem-tips*.
    Flowers February – April, also September – November.
    A hardy, extremely common little plant, forming large colonies
wherever there are sediment deposits from run-offs to the plain
or in *wadis* and depressions in desert areas and utilising the
heavy dewfall of September and October to produce leaves and
flowers in spite of the absence of rain. Its fragile branches are
easily demolished by vehicles careering over the terrain and by
the trampling feet of camels and goats, otherwise the plant
would increase in size and number, thus augmenting ground
cover.

*   *Helianthemum ledifolium* (L.) Mill.   R.G. 1950.

*   *Helianthemum salicifolium* (L.) Mill.   R.G. 1950.

*p.19

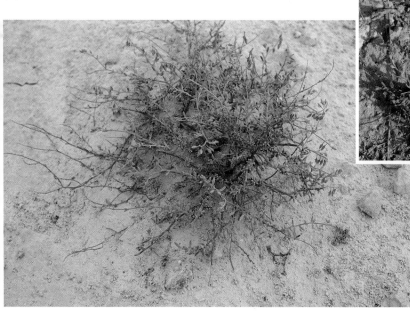

37A Helianthemum kahiricum

37B Helianthemum kahiricum

▲
◀ *Helianthemum* species

39A Anastatica hierochuntica

39B

39C

Anastatica hierochuntica

39D Anastatica hierochuntica

39E Anastatica hierochuntica Fruit

CUCURBITACEAE (Gourd Family)

Herbs climbing by tendrils, with large, usually deeply lobed leaves.
Flowers with united petals; fruit a kind of berry with a hard shell.

Citrullus colocynthis (L.) Schrad.   *
   =*Cucumis colocynthis* L.
Stems long, trailing; flowers yellowish; corolla 5-lobed; fruit a
small round gourd, mottled green, turning yellow.

B.N.H.S 1987.

CRUCIFERAE (Brassicaceae, Mustard Family)

Herbs with flowers that have 4 petals in the form of a cross, 4
sepals and 6 stamens and with seeds in long or short fruiting pods.

Anastatica hierochuntica L.   Ed. Herb. 193/4   *39*

A small prostrate annual found in compact gravelly soil
containing alluvial deposits, where the backslopes level out to
meet the plain near Hamad Town, Sakhir or Farsiyah. Leaves
15mm long, obovate-spathulate, faintly notched, tapering
towards a petiole. Flowers white, 3mm across. Silicle c 2mm long
with 1 pale yellowish-brown seed in each locule; each valve has a
hard ear-like appendage at its tip. As the plant matures its stems
become woody and curl inwards around the seed pods, while
most of the leaves drop. It will only uncurl to release seeds when
thoroughly moistened, thus ensuring availability of sufficient
moisture for them to germinate. Seeds are not widely distributed,
therefore many new plants grow in the vicinity of the old ones.
   Flowers in March, or after rain.
   Arabic name: '*Kaff Maryam*'.
   English name: 'The Jericho Rose'.
   The plant is known as 'The Virgin's Hand'; a name originating
   from a folk tale about Mary clutching one of these little plants
   in her hand during Christ's birth. Widely used as a charm for
   childbirth, it also has reputed medicinal value.

CRUCIFERAE

*   *Brassica tournefortii* Gouan
Flower pale yellow; silique terete, beaked.   Ed. Rec.

*   *Diplotaxis harra* (Forssk.) Boiss.
Flower bright yellow; silique deflexed, linear, beak very short.
        Ed. Rec.

*   *Eruca sativa* Mill.

Flower yellow, purple-veined; silique linear-oblong, beaked;
beak nearly as long as valves.
        Ed. Rec.

*   *Erucaria hispanica* (L.) Druce
        R.G. 1950.

40 *Farsetia heliophila* Bge.   Ed. Herb. 7, 192, 355
Perennial plant with many stiff erect slender stems, up to 25cm
high, found in gravelly soils in *wadis* and depressions of the
north-west and south-east backslopes. Stems and leaves grey,
canescent; leaves few, linear, elliptical or lanceolate, 10 – 15mm
long. Flowers dark red, turning brown or orange, 4mm across.
Pods grey, linear, oblong, 20 – 25mm long; at maturity the two
valves split open from the base of the pod exposing pale brown
seeds.
    Flowers March – June.

40A

Farsetia heliophila

40C

40B Flowers

Fruit

41   *Raphanus raphanistrum*

42   *Raphanus sativus*

Morettia parviflora Boiss.   **∗**
Flower pink, minute; silique linear, c 10mm long.

                                                              Ed. Rec.

Raphanus raphanistrum L.   Ed. Herb. 120, 285   ***41***
An erect annual herb, c 25cm high; weed of gardens and date
plantations. Leaves and stems bright green, leaves pinnatifid.
Flowers cream, dark-veined, delicate, 12mm across. Pods linear,
30mm long, 4 – 6 seeded, slightly constricted between seeds, with
a short beak.
   Flowers March.

Raphanus sativus L.   Ed. Herb. 121, 168   ***42***
Much branched annual herb, around 50cm high; a weed in
gardens and fields. Leaves large, pale green, pinnatifid. Flowers
mauve, 10mm across. Pods broad, beaked.
   Flowers March – June.
   A cultivated plant escaping and appearing as a weed. Its fleshy
root is the radish, a salad vegetable.

CRUCIFERAE

43 *Savignya parviflora* (Del.) Webb   Ed. Herb. 31
Delicate annual herb 15cm high, found on a stony slope on the
west side of the Jebel and in a gravelly *wadi* near Hamad Town.
Leaves 20 – 30mm long; lower leaves broad and lobed; upper
leaves linear. Flowers 5mm across, pale mauve. Silicle c 15 x
7mm, with silvery membranous central partition.
  Flowers February – March.

* *Sisymbrium irio* L.   Ed. Herb. 278

Slender erect herb with few branches, c 60cm high; weed of fields
and gardens. Leaves pinnatifid almost to the midrib, 70mm long.
Flowers small, pale yellow. Pods narrow, 1 – 2mm x 75mm, held
close to the stem.
  Flowers April.

43A

Savignya parviflora

Fruit ▶

43B

44A

Capparis spinosa ▶
▼

44B

44C

▲
◀ *Capparis spinosa* Fruit

44D

CAPPARACEAE (Caper Family)

Shrubs with simple alternate leaves and spiny stipules. Flowers solitary, bilaterally symmetrical, with 4 sepals, 4 petals and long stamens. Fruit a many-seeded capsule.

Capparis spinosa L.   Ed. Herb. 135, 181   *44*

Shrub of procumbent straggly growth in open spaces, or profuse tangled bushy growth to a height of c 1.5m against walls or other vegetation. Growing in and around the ruins of Qala'at al-Bahrain near the north coast, and common near cultivated areas with high water-table. Leaves orbicular, with sharp hooked stipular spines, and a tiny prickle at the leaf tip. Flowers emit an attractive scent; large, 40mm across, with 4 sepals, 4 petals and numerous prominent stamens. Fruit pear-shaped, 30 – 50mm long; purplish-grey outer skin splits and rolls back when fruit is ripe, exposing a tempting bright-red sticky centre full of seeds.

Flowers March – April. Plants die back in December.

Buds and shoots pickled and eaten in Europe and Mediterranean countries.

The flowers open in the evening for pollination by night-flying moths attracted by their perfume, then shrivel and die soon after sunrise.

CLEOMACEAE

Herbs with simple alternate leaves. Flowers bilaterally symmetrical, in racemes. Fruit a many-seeded pod-like capsule.

45 *Cleome* cf *quinquenervia*   Ed. Herb. 234, 348

An uncommon perennial herb, only seen in a large *wadi* east of Hamad Town on the northern backslope. Main stem 30 – 50cm tall, with branches ascending from its base. The whole surface of the plant has stiff bristly hairs and glands; the glands exude a pungent sticky substance suggestive of resin. Leaves cordate, 10 – 20mm long. Corolla pale yellow with reddish-brown markings in its centre, 5mm long, sepals 4mm, stamens 10mm; petals in typical *Capparis* arrangement, in 2 pairs; the upper petals of *Cleome quinquenervia* are pointed, resembling fox ears. Pods 30mm long.

Flowers May and September.

45ᴬ

Cleome cf *quinquenervia* Flowers   *45ᴮ*

Cleome cf *quinquenervia*

Cleome cf *quinquenervia* Fruit

45ᶜ

46A *Ochradenus baccatus*

46B *Ochradenus baccatus* Flowers

46C

Ochradenus baccatus Fruit

RESEDACEAE (Mignonette Family)

Herbs or shrubs with simple alternate leaves, entire or lobed. Inflorescence a raceme or spike-like raceme. Fruit a capsule or berry

Ochradenus baccatus Del.   Ed. Herb. 24a/b   **46**

A hardy perennial shrub of vigorous growth, preferring stony or rocky habitats, on the Jebel or in *wadis*, runnels and depressions in the north-east quarter of the central depression and eastern backslope. Leaves linear, few. Flower-spikes yellow; flowers minute and without petals. Fruit a waxy globose berry, white when ripe*.

Flowers March – May, and through the year.

Flies swarm around the flowering bushes, although to human nostrils there is no particularly obvious scent.

The green stems are palatable to browsing animals, mainly goats, which strip the plants down to a few centimetres.

*p.19

47 *Oligomeris linifolia* (Vahl) McBride   Ed. Herb. 10

Annual herb, very common in gravelly sand in depressions with sediments after rain. An erect plant, 15 – 30cm high, with few branches. Leaves blue-green, linear, flat, sharply pointed, up to 80mm long. Flowers minute, but salmon-pink seed capsules conspicuous, 3 – 4mm wide; stem elongates when in fruiting stage.

Flowers March or after rain.

＊ *Reseda muricata* Presl

Leaves lobed, inflorescence a raceme of small white 6-petalled flowers. Capsules obovoid.

R.G. 1950.

＊ *Reseda stenostachya* Boiss.   B.N.H.S. 1987.

FRANKENIACEAE (Sea Heath Family)

Herbs tolerant of saline soil. Leaves opposite or whorled; flowers minute, with 5 petals; fruit a many-seeded capsule.

48 *Frankenia pulverulenta* L.   Ed. Herb. 49, 280

Prostrate mat-like annual herb, appearing in sandy soil near habitations and occasionally as a weed in gardens. Stems slender, reddish coloured; leaves fleshy, minute, deep green or reddish, oblong-spathulate, on short petioles, in pairs or clustered. Flowers pale pink, 2mm across, singly in axils. Many minute seeds form in capsules*.

Flowers March – April.

*p.18

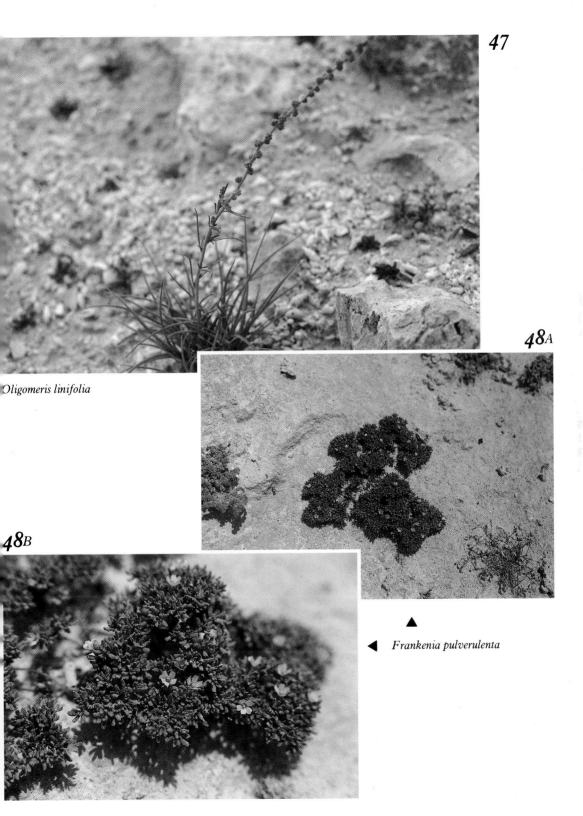

47

Oligomeris linifolia

48A

48B

Frankenia pulverulenta

49
Tamarix arabica

50A

Tamarix pycnocarpa with
Phragmites australis

50B

Tamarix pycnocarpa
Flowers and fruit

TAMARICACEAE (Tamarisk Family)
Shrubs or trees with alternate scale-like minute leaves and pink flowers in racemes. Fruit a many-seeded capsule.

Tamarix arabica DC.   Ed. Herb. 224, 282   **49**

Small isolated shrub in *sabkha* at the southern end of the central depression and along coasts, and larger bushy shrub or small tree in damp or swampy saline soil near towns and villages in northern areas. Height varying from .5m to 3m. Bark grey, young stems reddish-brown. Many slender branchlets with tiny clasping blue-green leaves give a soft outline to the shrub; leaves 3mm long, sharply pointed, with salt crystals on the surface*. Flowers pale pink, minute, in 20 – 60mm long spikes. Fruits conical, reddish, 4mm long; seeds have a tuft of silky hairs.
    Flowers January – April, and September.
    Arabic name: '*Ethl*' or '*Asla*'.
    The soft feathery profile of the 'Tamarisk' is a familiar feature of desert landscapes and salt marshes. It provides shelter and browsing for animals, also aids in controlling erosion of the soil, but is an extravagant water user with deep roots.

Tamarix pycnocarpa DC.   Ed. Herb. 236   **50**

Large bushy shrubs 2.5m high, bordering a small lake created by waste water from a factory in the central depression near the east rim rock where soil is fine and chalky. Bark greyish or reddish-brown, young shoots purplish; foliage bluish-green, feathery, composed of many fine stems with minute ovate clasping leaves; glands in the leaves excrete salts*. Inflorescences attractive soft cascading bright pink flower-spikes; flowers bisexual, 7mm across. Red conical fruits, 12mm long, contain numerous seeds with silky tufts.
    Flowers January and November.
    Arabic name: '*Ethl*'.

*pp.18, 19

PRIMULACEAE (Primrose Family)

Herbs with simple, opposite or alternate leaves. Flowers
5-petalled, solitary or in a raceme. Fruit a capsule with many
seeds.

*   *Anagallis arvensis* L. 'Pimpernel'
    (*Anagallis femina* Mill. R.G. 1950.)
    Flowers blue.   B.N.H.S. 1987.

*   *Samolus valerandi* L. 'Brook Weed'
                               R.G. 1950.

MALVACEAE (Mallow Family)

Herbs with palmately veined, lobed leaves. Flowers solitary or
clustered, in leaf-axils, with white petals and epicalyx. Fruit
circular, dividing at maturity into 1-seeded portions.

*   *Malva aegyptia* L.
    Leaves palmate-veined and cleft.
                                 D.B. 1979/81.

51 *Malva parviflora* L.   Ed. Herb. 256
Annual herb of gravelly depressions and *wadis*, also frequent in
irrigated areas. Most stems prostrate or procumbent with usually
one erect central stem; stems tough, pale green to reddish,
clothed with sparse stiff hairs. Leaves dark green, also with
minute stiff hairs; on long petioles, not deeply lobed. Flowers
5mm long, almost sessile, in clusters at nodes, with 5 sepals just
exceeding the 5 petals. The fruit is segmented, flattened,
capsule-like, with 10 carpels each containing 1 almost-black seed;
capsule within the papery epicalyx.
    Flowers February – April.
    Arabic name: '*Khubbaiza*'.

5I*A*

▲

Malva parviflora ▶

5I*B*

TILIACEAE

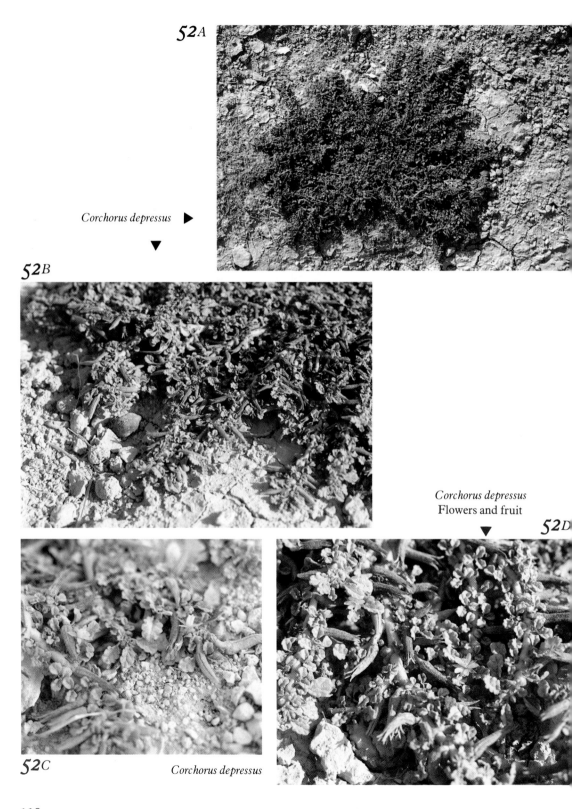

52A

Corchorus depressus ▶

▼

52B

Corchorus depressus
Flowers and fruit

▼

52D

52C

Corchorus depressus

TILIACEAE (Lime Family)

Herbs with alternate leaves and minute flowers. Fruit a many-seeded capsule.

Corchorus depressus (L.) Stocks   Ed. Herb. 343   *52*

Prostrate mat-like perennial, with relatively thick sturdy branches. Grows in compacted sandy soil in a *wadi* east of Hamad Town and is not common. Leaves abundant, dark green, oblong-almost orbicular, 5 – 8mm long, margins crenate and undulate. Flowers minute, yellow, 2mm long, 5-petalled, only open after noon. Length of capsule 10mm; capsules contain numerous 1mm long black seeds and open by apical teeth.

Flowers April and September.

EUPHORBIACEAE (Spurge Family)

Herbs or shrubs containing milky caustic juice that is often poisonous. Flowers lack petals. Inflorescence in Euphorbia species a *cyathium*, which resembles a single flower but is a group of simple unisexual flowers containing several male flowers around one central female flower all attached within a cup rimmed by glandular appendages; each male flower consists of a single stamen; the female flower is an ovary on a stalk. Fruit a capsule.

53 *Andrachne telephioides* L. Ed. Herb. 44, 157, 167

A small prostrate or procumbent shrub, common in gravelly compact soil in depressions, and protruding fern-like from stones and rocks on the Jebel. Stems slender, leaves dark bluish-green, 3 – 5mm long. Flowers minute, with 5 green sepals. Capsules green, globe-shaped, length 2 – 3mm.

Flowers March – May.

Almost disappears during dry seasons, but rapidly sends out long shoots after rain or heavy dew.

* *Euphorbia densa* Schrenk

Annual herb, up to 10cm high, seen in the central depression.

R.G. 1950.

53^A

Andrachne telephioides ▶
▼

53^B

53^C

Andrachne telephioides
Flowers and fruit

54

Euphorbia peplus

55

Euphorbia serpens

Euphorbia peplus L.   Ed. Herb. 100, 125   *54*

An erect, rather delicate pale green annual herb, c 10cm high,
growing as a weed around date plantations and gardens. Leaves
alternate or opposite, obovate or ovate. Inflorescences green
cyathia borne at the tips of umbel-like lateral branches. Fruit a
green 3-sided capsule, 2mm long, suspended on a tiny stalk from
the centre of the cup.
   Flowers March – May.

Euphorbia serpens Kunth   Ed. Herb. 231   *55*

Prostrate perennial growing in compact stony sediment in a *wadi*
east of Hamad Town. Stems woody at base and tortuously
twisting between stones. Leaves minute, deep green or reddish.
Flower groups minute, not more than 1mm across including their
surrounding glandular parts, which are dark red with pinkish
petal-like appendages; thus each cyathium resembles a pink
flower.
   Flowers February – March.

NEURADACEAE

Woolly herbs with simple alternate lobed leaves, solitary axillary flowers, and orbicular spiny fruits.

*   *Neurada procumbens* L.

An annual spreading prostrate herb found near villages where it is grazed by domestic animals. Leaves lobed small and woolly. Flowers minute, 5-petalled, yellowish. Its spiny orbicular fruits cling to animals' fur thus widely dispersing their seeds.

Arabic name: '*Sa'adan*'.

R.G. 1950, D.B. 1979/81.

CAESALPINIACEAE (Poinciana Family)

Shrubs with pinnate leaves, large irregular flowers and seeds in flattened pods.

56   *Cassia italica* (Mill.) F.W. Andrews   Ed. Herb. 139

A small shrub with procumbent branches bearing bright blue-green foliage, growing to a length of 50 – 75cm; in gravelly compact soil in depressions and run-off channels from the northern backslope. Each leaf has 3 – 5 pairs of leaflets in paripinnate formation. Flowers irregular, typical of this family; width of flower 20 – 25mm, corolla yellow. Fruits flat pods with rounded ends, 40mm x 15mm; the pods turn brown as they ripen*.

Flowers February – June.

Arabic name: '*Ishrig*'.

Of wide repute as a medicinal plant; the pods and leaves are used for a mild purgative. They can be bought from the *suq Hawaj*.

Well known drug 'senna' comes from plants in this genus.

Recorded Jazirat Hawar C.C. 1983 and 1985.

*p.19 and illustration p.39

56A   *Cassia italica*

56B *Cassia italica* Flowers

56C *Cassia italica* Fruit

57ᴬ

Alhagi maurorum

57ᴮ

▲
Alhagi maurorum Flowers

57ᶜ

◀ *Alhagi maurorum* Fruit

LEGUMINOSAE (Fabaceae, Pea Family)

Herbs or shrubs with papilionaceous flowers, legumes (pods), and usually pinnate leaves.

Alhagi maurorum Medik.   Ed. Herb. 81, 175   **57**

A small green spiny shrub forming dense colonies in open ground near habitations, along roadsides and in fields where there is a fairly high water table and saline soil. Often appearing leafless as flowering plants have few leaves, and those are usually minute. Spines green, thick and fleshy, c 20mm long. Flowers 7mm long, pinkish-red. Pods 10 – 20mm long.

New shoots appear in February, even thrusting up through asphalt.

Flowers June – August. Plants die off in December.

Vernacular name: '*Heidj*' or '*Aagool*'.

Reputedly used in remedies for several ailments.

58 *Astragalus annularis* Forssk.

Tiny hairy annual herb just a few cm high, found in sandy soil at the edge of the northern backslope. Leaves with 2 – 3 pairs of leaflets. Flowers white, tinged purple. Pods c 40mm long, curving, with red streaks and blotches.

Flowers March.

59 *Astragalus corrugatus* Bertol.   Ed. Herb. 148, 247

Small annual herb, 8cm high, in silty depressions in the Dumistan area. Leaves with 5 – 8 pairs of leaflets, notched at the apex. Flowers white tinged with purple, 5mm long, in groups of 2 – 3, on axillary peduncles. Pods c 20 – 30mm long, sickle-shaped, with a corrugated surface.

Flowers March, or after rain.

* *Astragalus hauarensis* Boiss.

Pods 30 – 40mm long, semicircular.   R.G. 1950.

* *Astragalus schimperi* Boiss.

Pods c 20mm long, narrow, curved.   R.G. 1950.

60 *Astragalus tribuloides* Del.   Ed. Herb. 26

Small prostrate hairy annual with stems c 10cm long. Leaflets in 6 – 9 pairs. Flowers purplish-white, clustered at axils. Pods c 10mm long, slightly curved.

58

Astragalus annularis

59   *Astragalus corrugatus*

60   *Astragalus tribuloides*

61A

Hippocrepis bicontorta

61B

61C

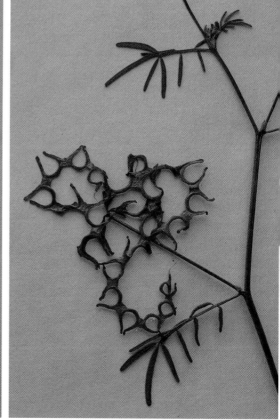

Hippocrepis bicontorta Lois.   Ed. Herb. 23   *61*

A prostrate annual herb with several spreading branches; fairly common in depressions with sandy soil, in the central depression and at the foot of backslopes. Flowers yellow, 6mm long, in small clusters. Coiled pods, with horseshoe-shaped joints, ensure that seeds enter the soil by almost screwing them into the ground.
    Flowers March – April.

Hippocrepis unisiliquosa L.   *

Pods not coiled, openings in joints almost closed.

                                                                    R.G. 1950.

62 *Lotus halophilus* Boiss. & Sprun.   Ed. Herb. 9
   =*L. pusillus* Viv.
Prostrate hairy annual herb with branches 10 – 15cm long,
growing in many localities in depressions where sediments gather.
Leaflets in groups of 5. Flowers pale yellow, c 4mm long. Pods
linear, 15 – 20mm x 1 – 1.5mm; when ripe they split open and
twist to eject their seeds.
   Flowers March.

63 *Lotus garcinii* DC.   Ed. Herb. 21, 142, 151
A tiny hairy shrub with erect and procumbent branches forming
clumps 10 – 30cm high, in soft sand on the plain east of
Dumistan. Stems and leaves grey-green; leaflets very small, in
groups of 5, almost clustered. Flowers pale pink, red-veined,
5mm long. Pods 7mm long.
   Flowers March – April.

* *Lotus glinoides* Del.
Flowers pink, small. Pods c 20mm long. Seen only on Jebel
Dukhan.

R.G. 1950.

62

63B

Lotus halophilus

Lotus garcinii ▶

63C

63A

63D *Lotus garcinii*

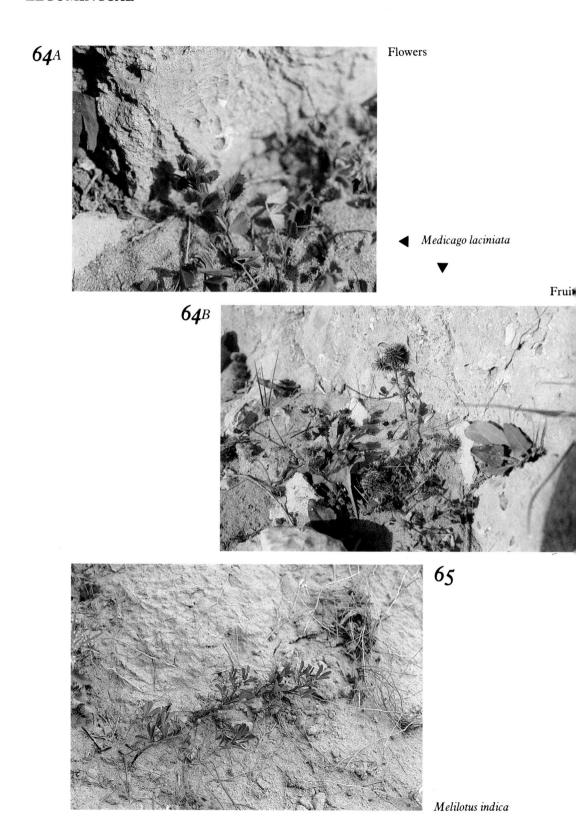

64A

Flowers

◄ *Medicago laciniata*

▼

Frui

64B

65

Melilotus indica

Medicago laciniata (L.) Mill.   Ed. Herb. 25, 146   **64**

Small annual dark green herb, found in various localities; in fine soils in gardens, *wadis*, depressions and waste places, also on the Jebel below a leaking water tank. Branches often prostrate. Leaves trifoliate, leaflets serrate-margined. Flowers pale yellow. Pods tightly coiled, almost spherical, spinous.
   Flowers March.

Melilotus indica (L.) All.   Ed. Herb. 1a/b/c, 126   **65**

An annual herb, c 25 – 30cm high, usually growing abundantly in irrigated fields, in and near cultivated areas, but recorded also in a depression near the Tree of Life*. Leaves trifoliate; leaflets obovate, notched at apex. Flowers yellow, minute, 1 – 2mm long, in long clusters or racemes from axils. Pods about 2mm long.
   Flowers March – May.
   Mature plants develop a powdery bloom and smell pleasantly of coumarin, a substance contained in their leaves and stems.

Melilotus alba Medic.   Ed. Herb. 30   **∗**

Similar to *M. indica* but plants more slender, with white slightly larger flowers and longer racemes. A weed where there is loamy soil and irrigation.
   Flowers April.

*p.30

*   *Ononis reclinata* L. 'Small Restharrow'
    Flower mauve; fruiting pedicel deflexed.

R.G. 1950.

*   *Ononis serrata* Forssk.
    Flower pink; pod small, ovoid.

R.G. 1950.

66 *Taverniera aegyptiaca* Boiss.   Ed. Herb. 154, 249
    Shrublet with stiff slender blue-green branches, 20 – 50cm tall,
    growing in piled sand inside the south-east rimrock, also near
    Dumistan (towards the north-west). Leaves blue-green, oval,
    minute to 6mm. Attractive when in flower, with pink pea-flowers
    contrasting blue-green foliage. Flowers 7mm long; corolla with
    pinkish-red veins. Fruit a flat pod of 2 or 3 disc-like segments
    with red bristles*.
        Flowers February – March.

*Illustration p.37

66A   *Taverniera aegyptiaca* Flowering

66B
Taverniera aegyptiaca Fruit

LEGUMINOSAE

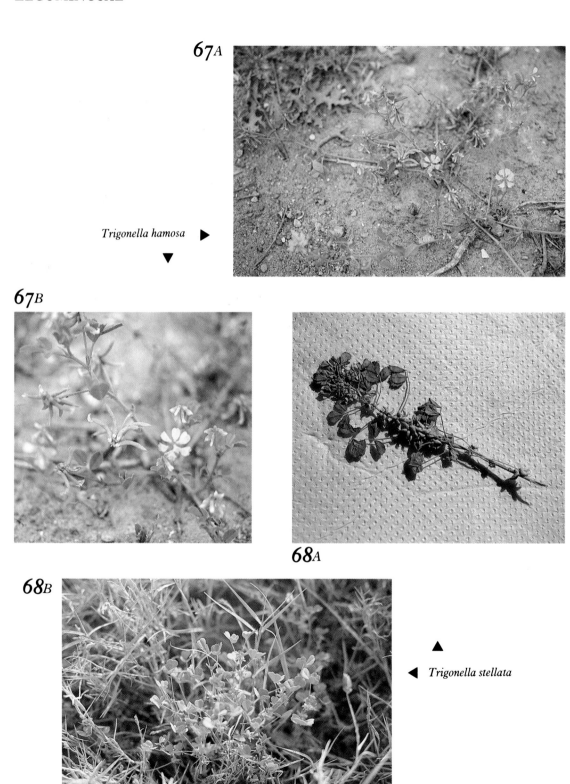

67A

Trigonella hamosa ▶
▼

67B

68A

68B

▲
◀ *Trigonella stellata*

138

Trigonella anguina Del.   Ed. Herb. 28b   *

Small annual prostrate herb growing in fine sand and sediment in depressions near villages by the northern backslope. It has trifoliate leaves with dentate-margined leaflets. The minute pale yellow flowers are on very short stalks in the leaf axils. Pods c 7mm long, pleated, in star-shaped clusters.

Flowers March or after rain.

Trigonella hamosa L.   Ed. Herb. 255   **67**

Annual herb with procumbent stems up to 20cm long branching from its base; found near Sar in gravelly sand. Leaves trifoliate, leaflets obovate, notched at the apex. Flowers 4mm long, clustered, on long peduncles. Pod c 10mm long.

Trigonella stellata Forssk.   Ed. Herb. 28a, 149   **68**

Bright green herb, prostrate in open ground, erect among other plants; it spreads quickly and profusely, providing good grazing; common in all localities where water deposits sediments in depressions and *wadis*, also in gullies on Jebel Dukhan. Leaves trifoliate, with obcordate leaflets. Flowers bright yellow, 2mm long, almost sessile, in axillary clusters. Pods c 7mm long, slightly curved, in stellate clusters.

Flowers February – April.
Arabic name: '*Nafal*'.

Vicia monantha Retz.   *

Leaves paripinnate, central leaf-stem terminating in a tendril. Flowers mauve.

R.G. 1950.

MIMOSACEAE (Mimosa Family)

Shrubs or trees with thorns and/or prickles and bipinnate leaves. The minute flowers are in globose heads or spikes and the fruit is a legume.

* *Acacia* species
Usually tall trees, but browsed intensively by camels and goats to small shrubs c 1.5m high, occasionally reaching 2.5m. Only seen on the sandy plain south of Sar. Bark reddish-brown*.

* *Acacia tortilis* (Forssk.) Hayne subsp. *raddiana* (Savi) Brenan
Tall flat-topped trees with reddish-brown bark and two kinds of stipular spine, long and straight or short and hooked backwards, in pairs. Leaves usually with three or more pairs of pinnae. Flowers creamy-white, in globular heads c 8mm in diameter. Pods yellowish-brown, c 100mm long, spirally twisted.
Recorded along the foot of the backslope south of Sar.
K.V. 1978/79.

69 *Prosopis farcta* (Banks & Sol.) McBride   Ed. Herb. 136, 155, 180
Small spiny shrub speedily and effectively colonising dry abandoned fields with poor stony soil, and forming roadside borders near habitations. Branches grey and untidy but forming compact bushes up to 50cm high; leaflets minute. Inflorescences of soft cylindrical spikes of minute flowers, like catkins. The rounded pinkish-purple pods gradually turn black and harden into grotesque shapes.
New foliage March, flowers April.
Vernacular name: '*Yambut*'.

*p.19

69A

Prosopis farcta Flowering

69B

Prosopis farcta With fruit

MIMOSACEAE

70A

Prosopis juliflora   Flowers and fruit

70B

Prosopis juliflora Flowering

Prosopis juliflora (Sw.) DC.   Ed. Herb. 134, 208, 275   **70**

Flat-topped bushy tree, 3 – 8m tall, with pendulous branches, lining roads and appearing singly or in groves around villages. Bark grey or reddish, peeling underneath. Spines straight, axillary, usually paired. Leaves with 1 – 3 pairs of pinnae and 13 – 20 pairs of leaflets in each pinna; leaflets oblong, 6 – 12mm long. Inflorescences are catkin-like cylindrical spikes of pale yellow flowers. Pods straw-coloured, 100 – 150mm long*.

Flowers May and September.

A relative of the Central American 'mesquite', this species was introduced and planted as a shade tree along roads. It has since become well-established in desert as well as irrigated soils and forms pleasant shady groves, particularly in the Sakhir area. The pods are nutritious and valuable as fodder, but the foliage is apparently unpalatable as it is never browsed.

*pp.19, 30 and illustrations pp.30, 38

CYNOMORIACEAE

Fleshy leafless herbs without chlorophyll, parasitic on roots.
Flowers minute, simple; male flowers with one stamen. The fruit
is nut-like.

7I *Cynomorium coccineum* L. Ed. Herb. 98

This intriguing parasitic plant can be seen poking up out of the
soft sand around its host and source of nourishment, *Zygophyllum
qatarense*. Varying in size from 7 – 20cm high, it consists of
minute red fleshy flowers, both male and female, clustered over a
thick fleshy spadix, which has a few vestigial leaves in the form of
brown scales at its base. Pollination is ensured by the many flies
attracted to the flowers by their foetid odour*.

Flowers January – February, after rain.

English name: 'Desert Thumb'.

Occurs here and there in the central depression, but is most
frequent in wind-blown sand by the south-west rim rock.

RUTACEAE (Citrus, Rue Family)

*   *Haplophyllum* species

Recorded only on eastern backslope.   R.G. 1950.

*Illustration p.33

7I *Cynomorium coccineum* and *Zygophyllum qatarense*

GERANIACEAE

72A

72B

Erodium glaucophyllum ▲ ▶ ▼

72C Fruit

72D *Erodium glaucophyllum*

GERANIACEAE (Geranium Family)

Herbs with lobed or pinnatisect leaves and 5-petalled flowers in umbellate clusters. The fruit is long-beaked, with 5 seeds.

Erodium glaucophyllum (L.) L'Hér.   Ed. Herb. 16, 42, 237   *72*

Perennial herb providing welcome splashes of bright green along desert roads in the central depression; also frequent on the Jebel in sandy nooks. It has profuse growth of petioled broad tough leaves at its base with many pale green stems branching and ascending to c 25cm. Leaves 20 – 40mm long, faintly lobed, margins slightly indented; colour bright bluish-green with a whitish bloom due to a sparse covering of minute hairs. Inflorescence a 3 – 5-flowered umbel; flowers purplish-pink, 5-petalled, 7 – 10mm long. Fruit 50 – 80mm long, comprising 5 seeds each 4mm long and provided with a feathery plume; the plumes are twisted together at the base and tightly packed forming a beak; at maturity they unwind then detach from the tip for efficient seed dispersal by wind.

Flowers February – April.

The plant combats dry conditions by retaining reserves of moisture within thickened sections in its roots.

73 *Erodium laciniatum* (Cav.) Willd.   Ed. Herb. 147, 241
A slender herb, 10cm high, with procumbent or erect stems and
blue-green pinnatifid lace-margined leaves. It appears in
favourable habitats that have some moisture and fine soil with
sediments, in *wadis* and depressions; recorded in the *wadi* east of
Hamad Town, near Dumistan, and on the Jebel below a (leaking)
water tank. Leaves 5 – 30mm long; flowers delicate, pale pink,
purple-veined, 5mm across. Beaked fruits 40mm long split from
the base into 5 slender valves around a central column.
   Flowers February – April.

74 *Monsonia nivea* (Dcne.) Webb   Ed. Herb. 6, 111
Small perennial herb, 7 – 10cm high, with silvery leaves;
associated with *Heliotropium ramosissimum* in soft sand east of Ras
Noma and in the south-east quarter of the central depression.
Leaves ovate-oblong, hairy. Flowers delicate pink, 5-petalled,
5mm across. Fruits beaked, 35mm long; 5 achenes on silky
plumes are released from the base of the beak, leaving behind a
central column.
   Flowers February – April.
   These small plants reach way down to underground moisture
layers by means of long thick roots which are out of all
proportion to their growth above ground.

LINACEAE (Flax Family)

*   *Linum strictum* L.

R.G. 1950.

73^A

Erodium laciniatum ▶
▼

73^B   Fruiting

74^A

▲
◀ *Monsonia nivea*
▼

74^B

74^C   After seed dispersal

ZYGOPHYLLACEAE

75 *Fagonia* species

ZYGOPHYLLACEAE (Bean Caper, Caltrop Family)

Shrubs or herbs with opposite or alternate leaves; leaves 2 – 3
foliate or simple. Flowers with 5 sepals and 5 petals or lacking
petals. Fruit a capsule.

Fagonia bruguieri DC.   Ed. Herb. 290   *

Perennial spiny shrublet, 10 – 15cm high, with many horizontal
lateral branches spreading out from a woody short central stem.
Growing in gravelly sand in a *wadi* east of Hamad Town and in
the central depression. Foliage pale green, lower leaves trifoliate,
upper leaves unifoliate, elliptic-lanceolate. Flowers 5-petalled,
mauvish-pink, 6mm across. Capsule 3 – 4mm long,
onion-shaped, with 5 segments.
    Flowers March – May.

Fagonia indica Burm.f.   **75**

Perennial procumbently branched spiny shrublet, 10 – 15cm
high, widespread in sandy and rocky places including the western
slopes of the Jebel. Leaves oval-lanceolate or oblong, c 10mm
long; spines varying in length, 7 – 15mm long. Flowers
mauvish-pink, 6mm across. Capsule ridged, onion-shaped, 3 –
4mm long.
    Flowers March – May. Dies right back in dry seasons.
    Arabic name: '*Shukkah*'.
    Fagonia species are widely distributed and common in most
areas except those continually under cultivation. The plants
often remain small as they are a food plant of Spiny-tailed
lizards and camels.
    Fagonia species recorded Hawar island group C.C. 1983.

76 *Fagonia ovalifolia* Hadidi   Ed. Herb. 17, 110

A spiny shrublet, similar to *F. indica* but with broader leaves, growing in loose sand in the south-east section of the central depression and in the sandy borders along the Tubli Bay road. Lower leaves petiolate, upper leaves sessile.

   Flowers March – May and September – October.

77 *Seetzenia lanata* (Willd.) Bullock   Ed. Herb. 8

Prostrate green herb with branches 15cm long radiating from its base. Uncommon and only found in sandy soil in a *wadi* near the Tree of Life*.

Leaves bright green, trifoliate, with leaflets 4mm long. Flowers very small, green, inconspicuous, 5-sepalled, lacking petals. Fruit more noticeable; a yellow capsule showing from inside its surrounding green sepals; capsule 3 – 4mm long.

   Flowers January – February.

＊   *Tribulus pentandrus* Forssk.

B.N.H.S. 1987.

*p.30

76   *Fagonia ovalifolia*

77ᴮ ▲

◀   *Seetzenia lanata*

77ᴬ

ZYGOPHYLLACEAE

78A

Zygophyllum qatarense

78B   Flower

78C   Fruit

Zygophyllum qatarense Hadidi Ed. Herb. 13, 131, 299, 365 **78**

This small shrub is Bahrain's most common and dominant plant. Its many tough woody branches bear succulent leaves on fleshy cylindrical bright green petioles. The leaves are usually bifoliate, but during prolonged drought, mostly simple leaves are produced, or the second leaflet drops; leaflets bright green, 5mm long, almost spherical. Flowers solitary, on short pedicels, creamy-white, 5-petalled, 5mm long. Fruit capsules oblong-pear-shaped, 8mm long.

Flowers March – May and sporadically September – November.

Arabic name: '*Harm*'.

An extraordinary plant which remains green through months of severe heat and drought. Its rounded clumps with their attendant sand hummocks are a constant feature of Bahrain's landscape. In the hot months heat shimmer transforms them into mirages of mysterious floating islands. During prolonged dry weather the plants are able to close off all but a few of their branches, just retaining a minimum of living cells until there is moisture enough for regrowth*. Secreted salts, from the saline soil, help to retain moisture in the succulent parts and apparently render the plants unpalatable to browsing animals. Recorded Hawar island group C.C. 1983 & 1985.

*pp.18, 19 and illustration p.28

79 *Zygophyllum simplex* L.   Ed. Herb. 14

Annual plant with slender branching yellowish or purple stems spreading close to the ground; stems with abundant fleshy bright green cylindrical leaves and yellow flowers. Leaves simple, alternate, length 5 – 10mm. Flowers solitary, 5-petalled, 4mm wide. Fruit a tiny spherical capsule 2mm long.

Flowers April – June, and September – November.

An extremely common plant, appearing after rain in all desert localities and hillsides regardless of soil.

Recorded Hawar island group C.C. 1983.

UMBELLIFERAE (Apiaceae, Parsley Family)

Herbs with usually divided leaves and minute flowers in umbels. Fruit dry, 2-chambered, separating when ripe into two 1-seeded carpels.

*   *Anethum graveolens* L.   Ed. Herb. 122

Erect green herb, 30 – 50cm high, in and around gardens and cultivation. Leaves strongly aromatic, divided into long filiform segments. The minute yellow flowers are borne on many-stemmed umbels.

Flowers March and through the year.

Vernacular name: '*Shevad*'.

English name: 'Dill'.

The plant is cultivated for its seeds and leaves. The leaves are used dried or fresh as a potherb to flavour rice dishes. It also grows wild near irrigation.

*   *Apium graveolens* L. 'Wild Celery'

With white umbellate flowers and leaves with broad segments.

Only seen in cultivated areas.

R.G. 1950.

*   *Bupleurum semicompositum* L.

Recorded only on eastern backslope.

R.G. 1950.

79A   *Zygophyllum simplex*

79B   *Zygophyllum simplex*

80A

Ziziphus nummularia

80B

Flowers

80C

▲

◄ *Ziziphus nummularia*

Fruit

RHAMNACEAE (Buckthorn Family)

Shrubs or trees with simple alternate leaves; flowers with 5 sepals, 5 petals and 5 stamens, in axillary clusters; fruit a drupe.

Ziziphus nummularia (Burm. f.) Wight & Arn.   Ed. Herb. 188   ***80***

Thorny shrubs forming dense green thickets in a large *wadi* east of Hamad Town. Leaves glossy, prominently nerved. Flowers yellowish-green, fleshy, 4mm across. Fruits globose, orange to red, fleshy with a large hard seed in the centre, c 8mm long*.

  Flowers April – June and September – November, with fruits swiftly following the flowers.
  Many butterflies, bees and flies are attracted to the flowers by their inviting scent. The fruits are edible and have a pleasant taste.

Ziziphus spina-christi (L.) Willd.   Ed. Herb. 102, 209, 264   *

A small prickly shrub growing wild in abandoned fields, or a cultivated tall tree without spines. The cultivated trees have much larger leaves and larger more fleshy fruits than the wild variety. Fruits c 15mm in diameter, resembling miniature apples.

  Arabic name for the tree is '*Sidr*', and the fruits are '*Dum*'.
  A soothing eye bath can be concocted by steeping the leaves in water, or they can be used in a shampoo. Harvested fruits are sold in the *suq*.

*p.19

APOCYNACEAE (Dogbane Family)

Herbs containing milky juice, with simple opposite leaves.
Flowers with 5 joined petals are borne in clusters. Fruit a pair of
slender pods.

81 *Trachomitum venetum* (L.) Woodson   Ed. Herb. 183, 210

A perennial shrubby plant, rare on Bahrain, only seen in a dry
sandy ditch by the north side of the Budaiya road between
Janusan and Barbar. It has tough stems, up to 40cm high,
containing copious amounts of white sap. Leaves smooth,
ovate-oblong, rounded at the tip, 50mm long. The sweet-scented
white flowers are bell-shaped, 8mm long. Fruits are long narrow
pod-like follicles, 150 x 4mm, but propagation is mainly
vegetative, by rhizomes.

New shoots February, flowers May – October.

White sap flows when a leaf or branch is broken off and all the
nearby axils weep sap in sympathy.

81A

Trachomitum venetum

81C   *Trachomitum venetum*

81B

Trachomitum venetum with *Sesuvium verrucosum* (foreground),
Prosopis farcta and *Suaeda vermiculata*

82A

82B

▲

◄ *Glossonema varians*

▼

82C

ASCLEPIADACEAE (Milkweed Family)

Shrubs or herbs with usually opposite leaves and flowers borne in small axillary clusters. Fruit linear, pod-like or ovoid, containing numerous seeds.

Calotropis procera (Ait.) Ait.f.

Tree or tall shrub, poisonous, with milky juice. Leaves grey-green, large, thick, oblong-obovate. Flowers white, pink-purple-tipped, c 20mm across. Fruit green, globose or pear-shaped, smooth, containing many flat seeds with tufts of hairs*.

Arabic name: '*Osher*'.

English name: 'Apple of Sodom'.

M.M.Z. 1978.

Glossonema varians (Stocks) Benth.   Ed. Herb. 38   *82*

Perennial small herb, common on the western slopes of the Jebel, and growing locally in some *wadis* and depressions in gravelly sand. It only reaches a height of 15cm but its large soft hairy leaves attract the eye. Leaves blue-green, often greyish, ovate, with crinkled margins, 10 – 25mm long. The waxy flowers are on short pedicels in the axils; flowers with 5 small hairy sepals and pale yellow petals, 4mm across. Conspicuous ovoid fruits, 30mm long, with soft spines, contain flat seeds, each in a papery envelope furnished with a silky tuft.

Flowers February – October.

Arabic name: '*Itr*'.

*Illustration p.37

83 *Leptadenia pyrotechnica* (Forssk.) Dcne.   Ed. Herb. 84, 356
Dense bushy shrub composed of a thick woody stem with erect
branches up to 5m high, only growing in one area, in the deep
wind-blown sand in *wadis* through the south-western rim rock
and on the nearby sandy plain of Al Markh. New branches
smooth, green, usually leafless; leaves when present linear, 30mm
long*[1]. Flowers in well-spaced clusters along stems, fleshy,
yellowish-green, 4mm across, with 5 minute sepals; central parts
of flower fused into a fleshy cone. Pendulous pod-like follicles
split lengthwise to disperse their seeds; follicles 80mm long,
usually single but occasionally paired; seeds flat, each in a papery
envelope with a silky tuft*[2].
   Flowers January – March and September – November.
   Arabic name: '*Markh*'.
   English name: 'Broom bush' or 'Burning bush'.
   The most exciting aspect of this shrub is its fragrance when in
bloom. The air all around becomes diffused with its sweet
slightly intoxicating aroma, which of course attracts many
winged insects to pollinate its flowers. It is a food plant of
Danaus chrysippus (Plain tiger) butterfly larvae. Gazelle, hare,
birds and many other small animals find shade and shelter
beneath its dense branches. *Photosynthesis* is carried on in the
green stems as leaves are rarely present. The only bushes ever
seen bearing leaves had been severely cropped by browsing
camels. This unusual production of leaves seemed like a
desperate measure to provide photosynthetic material after
depletion of the green stems.
Recorded Jazirat Hawar C.C. 1983.

*[1]. p.19
*[2]. Illustration p.25

83A

Leptadenia pyrotechnica

83C *Leptadenia pyrotechnica* Fruit

83B *Leptadenia pyrotechnica* Flowers

84A

◀ *Centaurium pulchellum*
▼

84C

84B

GENTIANACEAE (Gentian Family)
Herbs with simple opposite leaves and showy 5-petalled flowers; fruit a many-seeded capsule.

Centaurium pulchellum (Sw.) Druce   Ed. Herb. 225, 243   **84**

Annual herb, not tolerant of drought, occurring only where there is irrigation in gardens and farms, also below the water-tank (occasionally overflowing) on the Jebel. It has bright green glabrous foliage and reaches a height of 30cm. Leaves lanceolate-oblong. Flowers c 8mm long, on stalks of different lengths forming a corymb-type inflorescence. The minute seeds are in a long narrow capsule.

   Flowers January – April.
   English name: 'Lesser Centaury'.

RUBIACEAE (Madder Family)

Shrubs with opposite leaves; flowers with joined petals; fruit a nut.

85 *Gaillonia* species   Ed. Herb. 291

Pale green uncommon shrublet with numerous slender stiffly erect stems, found only in the large *wadi* east of Hamad Town, in soil of sediment mixed with gravel. Leaves linear, 10mm long. A papery toothed sheath clasps the stem and calyx of each flower; calyx 4mm long; flower tubular, corolla pale pink, 6mm long, with teeth. Fruit hard, nut-like, developing inside the elongating calyx.

Flowers April – May, also October.

Gaillonia crucianellioides Jaub. & Spach.

R.G. 1950.

85A

Gaillonia species

85B

85C

Gaillonia species ▶

▲

86B

Arnebia decumbens

86A

Arnebia decumbens

86C

Arnebia decumbens with calyx
artificially spread to reveal nutlets

87A

Arnebia hispidissima ▶

87B

BORAGINACEAE
(Borage, Forget-me-not Family)
Herbs or shrubs clothed with stiff hairs, and with simple alternate leaves, inflorescences of recurvate cymes, and fruits that divide at maturity into nutlets.

Arnebia decumbens (Vent.) Coss. & Kral.   Ed. Herb. 36   **86**

Annual pale green densely hispid herb, fairly common in the gravelly soil typical of the central depression, backslopes and Jebel slopes, after rain. The plants are small, 15 – 20cm high. Leaves elliptical-oblong, 10 – 20mm long. Flower tubular; the bright yellow 12mm long corolla almost hidden by the hairy calyx, which elongates as the fruit forms; fruit of 4 nutlets, each 2mm long.
   Flowers April.

Arnebia hispidissima (Lehm.) DC.   Ed. Herb. 11, 37, 165   **87**

The cheerful 'Arabian Primrose' can be seen in most parts of the desert, also on the Jebel, after rain. It is an annual herb, 10 – 20cm high, often forming large compact clumps where there is deep sand, its bright yellow flowers gleaming among deep green foliage. Stems, leaves and sepals have bristly hairs; leaves elliptical-oblong, 10 – 20mm long; flower 6mm wide, its base tubular, with corolla about twice the length of the calyx.
   Flowers March – May.
   Women formerly used the powdery red dust, that rubs off the thick dark-red roots of these plants, as a cosmetic.

Arnebia linearifolia DC.   **✱**

R.G. 1950.

BORAGINACEAE

88 *Echiochilon kotschyi* (Boiss.) Johnston   Ed. Herb. 262

Shrublet with a thick blackish woody stem and grey woody branches with many small grey-green leaves; found on the plains at the foot of the western and northern backslopes, in compact gravelly sand. Leaves hairy, elliptical, 5 – 7mm long, and sessile. Flowers c 6mm long; corolla of 5 white petals, tinged blue round the toothed limb and yellow in the centre, exceeds the calyx by 2mm.

Flowers March.

89 *Gastrocotyle hispida* (Forssk.) Bge.   Ed. Herb. 191
      =*Anchusa hispida* Forssk.

Prostrate annual green herb covered with bristly hairs, growing in compact soil with sediment in northern *wadis*. Branches 15cm long, radiating from the base. Leaves large, wavy-margined, oblong, c 20mm long. Flowers brilliant blue, barely 1mm broad, in the axils. Fruit globose, inside the hairy calyx.

Flowers April – June.

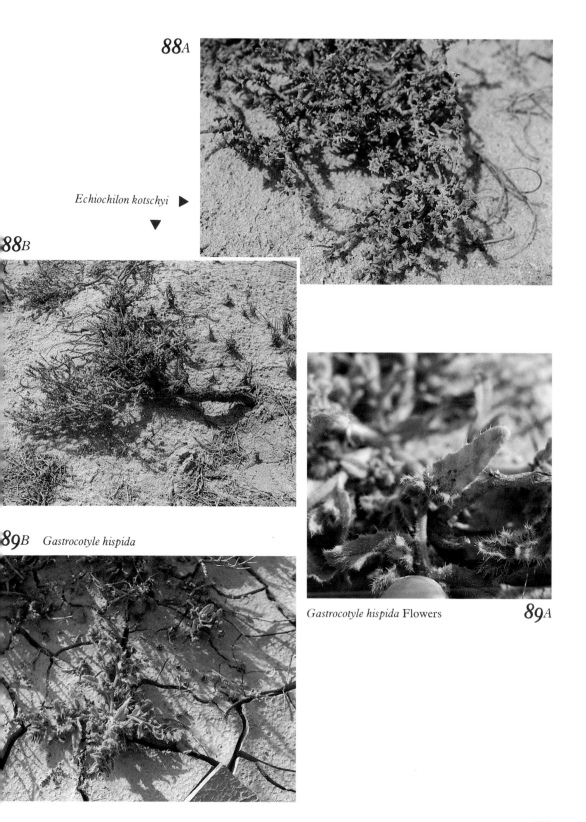

88A

Echiochilon kotschyi ▶
▼

88B

89B *Gastrocotyle hispida*

Gastrocotyle hispida Flowers   **89**A

BORAGINACEAE

90

Heliotropium currasavicum

91A

Heliotropium kotschyi ▶

91B

174

Heliotropium currasavicum L.   Ed. Herb. 118   **90**

Annual herb, 15cm high, with decumbent branches forming
bright blue-green carpets under date palms and by roadsides in
places with irrigation. Leaves spathulate, slightly fleshy, up to
60mm long. Minute white tubular flowers form a neat double row
along one side of each short flower-stem to its tip; cymes axillary
and terminal. Fruits globose, ripening into 4 hard brown nutlets.
   Flowers March – June.
   Arabic name: *'Kharees'*.
   Imported from S. America.

Heliotropium kotschyi (Bge.) Gürke   Ed. Herb. 65, 109, 257,   **91**
   301/2, 307

A widespread and common perennial shrublet forming dense
rounded bushes 50cm high, in depressions and *wadis* or on plains,
usually in gravelly soil. Leaves and stems are dark green, often
greyish, stiff, and rough with bristly hairs; leaves 10 – 40mm
long, slightly recurved. Up to 12 minute white 5-petalled flowers
lie close together along one side of each recurved flower stem, at
the tip. Fruits globose, with thickened white spongy border,
diameter 5mm; when ripe they separate into 4 nutlets; each pair
of nutlets attached centrally by a hard ring.
   Flowers March – April, and sporadically through the year.
   Arabic name: *'Rim ram'*.

92 *Heliotropium ramosissimum* (Lehm.) DC. Ed. Herb. 129
   =*H. crispum* Desf.

One of Bahrain's most widespread and common plants, a dark
green perennial shrublet dominating communities wherever there
is deep sand, particularly around Al Markh and in the south-east
quarter of the central depression. It has many branches,
sometimes spreading to form wide clumps, usually 30 – 40cm
high; the leaves and stems are crisp and rough with bristly hairs;*
leaves narrow, oblong-lanceolate, often revolute-margined.
Minute white tubular flowers, 5-sepalled and 5-petalled, forming
one-sided terminal cymes. Fruit globose, comprising 4 nutlets
encircled by a white spongy border and cupped within the hairy
calyx; it turns brown, dries out and separates at maturity.

Flowers March – May, and sporadically through the year.
This is the food plant of Crimson Speckled Moth larvae.
When threatened by drought the plant maintains just a few
green leaves at stem tips, occasionally transforming them into
swollen succulent reservoirs of moisture, while remaining
leaves and stems almost dry out.

*p.19

92A

Heliotropium ramosissimum

92B *Heliotropium ramosissimum* under dry conditions

93   *Moltkiopsis ciliata*

Lithospermum incrassatum Guss. R.G. 1950. ✳

Moltkiopsis ciliata (Forssk.) Johnst. Ed. Herb. 47, 141, 163 **93**
  =*Lithospermum callosum* Vahl
Perennial plant 10 – 15cm high, forming small clumps locally in
places with deep sandy soil; usually found in association with
Polycarpaea repens and *Monsonia nivea*, particularly among sand
dunes near Ras Noma. Leaves hairy, grey-green, oval,
ciliate-margined. Flowers on each curving stem in varying shades
of pink and blue, corolla tubular, 10mm long. Fruit of 4 nutlets,
each less than 1mm long, enclosed by the slightly elongated calyx.
  Flowers March – May.

Sericostoma persicum (Burm.f.) B.L. Burtt ✳
  R.G. 1950.

CONVOLVULACEAE (Morning Glory Family)
Herbs with simple alternate leaves and showy funnel-shaped
flowers with corolla of 5 united petals; fruit a capsule with usually
4 seeds.

94 *Convolvulus arvensis* L.   Ed. Herb. 127, 137
Creeping annual plant, aptly named 'Bindweed', which sends
long slender stems twining over other plants; only seen in areas
with loamy irrigated soil, where it is extremely common. It has
attractive sagittate leaves and showy pink or white
trumpet-flowers 15 – 20mm wide. Fruit an ovoid capsule
containing a few oval seeds.
   Flowers March onwards.
   Arabic name: *'Ollayq'*.

*   *Convolvulus deserti* Hochst.   B.N.H.S. 1987.

*   *Convolvulus lanatus* Vahl   R.G. 1950.

95 *Convolvulus* species   Ed. Herb. 161
Prostrate delicate herb, 4cm high, growing in deep sand in the
dune area east of Ras Noma. Leaves pubescent, pale green, 10 –
15mm long. Flowers funnel-shaped, pale pink, 10mm long.
   Flowers May.

94

Convolvulus arvensis

95

Convolvulus species

CONVOLVULACEAE

Convolvulus cf *pilosellifolius*

96B *Convolvulus* species

97 *Cressa cretica*

Convolvulus cf *pilosellifolius* Desr.   Ed. Herb. 19, 304, 351/2   **96**

Perennial herb with erect or prostrate branches, sometimes forming low cushion-like tufts, fairly common in the gravelly soil of *wadis* and depressions in the central depression and backslopes. Stems, leaves and sepals hairy; leaves greyish-green, oblong-elliptical. Flowers delicate pale pink, 7 – 10mm long, solitary, on axillary peduncles; flowers short-lived, blooming for just a few hours in the morning only. Fruit an ovoid capsule containing 4 minute oval seeds.

Flowers April and through the year when there is moisture.

Convolvulus pilosellifolius Desr.
R.G. 1950, B.N.H.S. 1987.

Cressa cretica L.   Ed. Herb. 90, 159, 197   **97**

Small perennial green herb, common in saline soils in northern areas, forming borders along roads and colonising waste ground. It has a central erect stem up to 15cm tall and lateral branches progressively shorter towards its tip creating a pyramid shape. Leaves minute, ovate, sessile, close together along stems. Flowers 4mm long, clustered at tips of stems; corolla pale pink, partly tubular with reflexed lobes and prominent mauve stamens. Fruit comprises a minute capsule with 3 – 4 seeds to which corolla and sepals are persistently attached. The whole plant is coated with salt crystals*.

Flowers May – June and September – October, then dies back until March.
Arabic names: '*Shuwayl*'; '*Nedeewah*'.

*p.18

CUSCUTACEAE (Dodder Family)

Leafless plants, parasitic on leaves and stems of other plants; with minute flowers in clusters and seeds in capsules.

98 *Cuscuta campestris* Yuncker (Pr. Det.)   Ed. Herb. 198, 359

A troublesome but fascinating parasitic plant, that densely drapes its pale orange filiform stems like cobwebs over herbaceous plants so its tiny sucker 'roots', *haustoria*, can fasten onto leaves and stems of its host to extract nourishment; it therefore needs no leaves or other parts containing chlorophyll. The flowers are on short pedicels, usually in threes; flowers white, 3mm long, with 5 inflexed petals, 5 stamens and 2 stigmas. Each tiny globose fruit has a thin membranous covering containing 4 seeds.

Flowers May and October.

The leaves of the host plant gradually die off followed in due course by branches; *Cuscuta* is thus regarded as a serious nuisance as it commonly parasitises alfalfa and other crops.

✻ *Cuscuta planiflora Ten.*

A plant very similar in appearance and habit to *C. campestris* but with thinner stems and flowers in conglomerate heads.

K.V. 1978/79.

Cuscuta planiflora is native to Middle Eastern countries, while *C. campestris*, native of N. America, was imported, probably among seed.

98A
Cuscuta campestris

98B
Cuscuta campestris

99^A

Cistanche tubulosa

99^B   *Cistanche tubulosa*   99^C

OROBANCHACEAE (Broomrape Family)
Succulent root parasites with scale-like leaves and showy
flower-spikes; fruit a capsule with many seeds.

Cistanche tubulosa (Schenk) Wight   Ed. Herb. 96/7, 235   **99**

A striking parasitic plant which erupts from the sand near its
host, *Zygophyllum qatarense*, after rain; on seashores hosts are
Suaeda vermiculata and *Arthrocnemum macrostachyum*. Its thick
fleshy stem, 30cm high or more, rises out of a bulbous root from
which a long threadlike root attaches to that of the host plant. The
parasite needs no chlorophyll as it depends on photosynthesis by
its host for nourishment; its leaves are vestigial, reduced to
brownish or purplish scales. Purplish buds cluster on the
flower-spike; flower subtended by 1 bract and 2 bracteoles; calyx
bell-shaped, corolla c 25mm long, waxy, short-lived, bright
yellow on seashores, bright yellow with pink or purple tube
inland. Hundreds of minute seeds disperse from an ovoid
capsule, 10mm long, which splits from its apex into 2 valves*.
  Flowers December – February.
  Arabic name: '*Dhanoon*'.
  Known in Bahrain as the 'Desert Tulip', also 'Desert
Hyacinth'.
  Though beautiful, these somewhat garish flowers tend to repel
rather than attract; a protective mechanism indicating perhaps
that poison is present.

*Illustrations pp.40, 188

99 *Cistanche tubulosa* on Suwad Al Janubiyah Island*

＊ *Orobanche cernua* Loefl.
Stem much thinner than that of Cistanche species; corolla tube
white, lobes blue.
    Occurrence infrequent.   R.G. 1950.

＊ *Orobanche mutelii* F. Schultz
Stem slender; flower violet.
    Western coastal region.   R.G. 1950.

*Fig. 3

PLANTAGINACEAE (Plantain Family)

Small green herbs with leaves rosetted at the base of plants and minute flowers crowded in ovoid or cylindrical spikes; fruit a membranous capsule.

Plantago coronopus L.   Ed. Herb. 145   *

Small green annual herb 5 – 8cm tall with long narrow leaves characteristically rosetted at its base and short cylindrical dense spikes of minute greenish flowers, each at the tip of a leafless stem or scape. Leaves oblong-lanceolate, lobed, 20 – 40mm long, all arising at the base of the plant. Flowers with green sepals, brownish petals and prominent stamens extending well beyond the petals.
  Flowers March – April.
  English name: 'Buck's-horn Plantain'.
  Found in depressions and *wadis* with sediment and moisture, particularly on the north-western backslope.

Plantago albicans L.   *
Found here and there in the cultivated zone and backslope.
R.G. 1950.

Plantago boissieri Hausskn. & Bornm.   *
  =*P. albicans* (non L.) Boiss.   B.N.H.S. 1987.

Plantago ciliata Desf.   *
B.N.H.S. 1987.

Plantago ovata Forssk.   *
Widely distributed on backslopes and central areas and found in the southern coastal region.
R.G. 1950.

SCROPHULARIACEAE
(Figwort, Snapdragon Family)

Herbs with simple or pinnatisect leaves. Flowers are solitary or in panicles or spike-like racemes; corolla with united petals, often 2-lipped. Fruit a capsule.

100 *Scrophularia deserti* Del.   Ed. Herb. 40, 41

Perennial woody-based herb, common in gravelly *wadis* in the central depression and rocky gullies on the Jebel. Leaves 10 – 20mm long and lobed, clustered at the base of the plant. The dark red flowers are 2 – 3mm wide; corolla bilabiate with 2 erect rounded upper lobes, small lower lip and rounded tube. Fruit a globose capsule 3mm long, from which the seeds disperse through a slit at the apex.

Flowers March – May. Plants die down in summer then new shoots appear November – February.

The 'rabbit-head' flowers are unusual and amusing.

* *Antirrhinum orontium* L.
=*Misopates orontium* (L.) Raf. 'Weasel's Snout'

R.G. 1950.

* *Herpestis monnieria* (L.) H.B.K.
=*Bacopa monnieri* (L.) Pennell   R.G. 1950.

Scrophularia deserti

Scrophularia deserti

SOLANACEAE

*101*A

Lycium shawii ▶
▼

*101*B

Fruit   *101*C

▲
◀ *Lycium shawii*

*101*D

SOLANACEAE (Nightshade Family)

Shrubs or herbs with simple alternate, sometimes opposite, leaves and flowers with united petals. Fruit a berry surrounded by the persistent calyx.

Lycium shawii Roem. & Schult.   Ed. Herb. 170, 187   *IOI*

Thorny shrubs of varying size up to 1.5m tall, widely distributed on all stony or rocky slopes and plains, but with some distance between each shrub. Their thorns are woody, extremely sharp and long; many lateral branches terminate in long thorns*. Leaves oblong or spathulate, very small, 6 – 10mm long, sometimes in clusters but often sparse or absent. Flowers solitary, mauvish-blue, pale or almost white in dry seasons, trumpet-shaped, 7mm long, with a small toothed calyx. Fruit a soft edible bright red berry, diameter 5mm.

Flowers March – May, and sporadically through the year.
Arabic name: *'Ausaj'*.
English name: 'Desert Thorn'.
The 'Desert Thorn' is a feature of the Bahrain landscape, presenting to the world a grey desiccated, somewhat forlorn aspect while unobtrusively, in the most adverse conditions of baking heat and aridity, continuing to produce a few bright green leaves, delicate flowers and juicy berries – pleasant surprises, revealed only by close scrutiny.
To the shrike it serves as a larder; left-overs can be impaled on the shrub's sharp thorns to await the bird's next meal time.
In leaf it provides browsing for camels and gazelle.
Recorded Hawar island group C.C. 1983 & 1985.

*p.19

102 *Withania somnifera* (L.) Dunal   Ed. Herb. 176, 202

An attractive green herbaceous shrub with few flexuous branches, only growing in loamy irrigated soil around fields and gardens. Its stems are whitish, tomentose, up to 1m tall. Leaves ovate c 60mm long. The pale green bell-shaped flowers are clustered in axils; length of flower 7mm; calyx woolly, enlarging to enclose the fruit, which is a globose bright red berry.

Flowers April – June.

Withania somnifera

102A

102B

AVICENNIACEAE

103^A

Avicennia marina with
Phoenix dactylifera

103^B

Avicennia marina Aerial roots

103^C

Avicennia marina

AVICENNIACEAE

Mangrove shrubs with simple opposite entire leaves and flowers in small terminal or axillary clusters. Fruit a 1-seeded capsule.

Avicennia marina (Forssk.) Vierh.   Ed. Herb. 189, 334   *103*

Evergreen shrubs with whitish branches and deep green foliage; height up to 2.5m, usually less. Habitat, swamp with tidal submersion and interwoven by streams from freshwater springs, around muddy marine inlet. The plants produce erect respiratory roots, *pneumatophores*, which protrude like shoots from the poorly aerated mud around their roots. Leaves leathery, glossy above, white underneath, ovate-oval, 60mm long. Flower-clusters are borne at tips of axillary peduncles; flowers waxy, exuding a heavy perfume, c 8mm long*. Fruit a single-seeded fleshy capsule. Mangrove seeds are viviparous, germinating and developing into seedlings before leaving the parent plant.

Flowers May – June.
English name: 'White Mangrove'.
White mangrove is a source of tannin.
The main mangrove colonies here, which are small, can be seen around Tubli Bay at Jurdab and Sanad. There are lesser colonies near Adhari, next to the highway north of Salmabad, and near Ikur.

*Illustration p.36

LABIATAE (Lamiaceae, Mint Family)

Aromatic herbs, often with 4-sided stems; leaves simple, opposite; flowers in heads or whorls, corolla usually 2-lipped; fruit of 4 nutlets in the calyx.

104 *Salvia aegyptiaca* L.   Ed. herb. 230, 303

Perennial faintly aromatic plant with thin stiff stems and numerous spreading branches 10 – 15cm high, growing locally in gravelly *wadis* and depressions in the northern backslope. The stems are hairy and 4-sided; leaves dark green, hairy, narrow, almost linear, crenate-margined, 10 – 20mm long. Flowers bilabiate, 5mm long; corolla white with blue spots in the throat, upper lip notched, lower lip divided into 3 lobes. Fruit of 4 ovoid blackish-grey nutlets inside the enlarged calyx.

Flowers March – May and October.

104A

Salvia aegyptiaca

104B

Salvia aegyptiaca Flower and fruit

*105*A

Teucrium polium

*105*B

Teucrium polium

Teucrium polium L. Ed. Herb. 15, 338 *105*

A hardy perennial woody-based herb with simple erect stems to a height of 30cm, common in stony habitats in *wadis* and runnels and on the Jebel. Stems, leaves and flower-heads are whitish-grey, soft with a felt-like covering of hairs. The aromatic leaves, in close, neatly opposite formation, are narrow, with crenate usually revolute margins, and 5 – 20mm long*. Flowers minute, white, with 4 red stamens; the 2 lobes of the small upper lip of the corolla lateral instead of dorsal, so that the lower lip appears to have 5 lobes instead of its actual 3. Fruit wrinkled, 1.5mm long.

Flowers April and through the year.

Arabic name: '*Ja'adh*'.

A medicinal plant of repute, said to be a fever curative, especially in cases of malaria and cholera, also a purgative taken as an infusion concocted from the leaves. May be purchased from the *Hawaj* in the *suq*.

*p.19

VERBENACEAE (Verbena Family)
Herbs with simple opposite leaves and minute flowers densely packed in axillary peduncled heads.

106 *Phyla nodiflora* (L.) Greene   Ed. Herb. 66, 87/8

Annual herb, 5 – 10cm high, forming dark green carpets of small plants by rooting from the nodes of creeping runners; along roadsides and in gardens where there is plenty of moisture. Leaves oval-spathulate, serrate-margined along the outer edge. Flowers in ovoid compact heads; corolla mauvish-pink, tubular, somewhat 2-lipped, 3mm long, between overlapping purplish bracts.

Flowers April – June.

COMPOSITAE (Asteraceae, Daisy Family)
Herbs or shrubs with inflorescences of small uni- or bisexual flowers, *florets*, closely packed in flat-topped heads, *capitula*, resembling single flowers; each head is subtended by an involucre of bracts like a calyx. The petals of each floret are fused into a tube, elongated on one side in ray florets to form a ligule or strap. Fruits are achenes, usually with an apical pappus, often consisting of a parachute of hairs or bristles.

107 *Aster squamatus* (Spr.) Hieron ex Sod.   Ed. Herb. 119, 204

A dark green erect perennial herb up to 1m high, with woody stems at the base, growing along borders of gardens and fields where there is moisture, and sometimes a troublesome weed. Leaves alternate, lanceolate-oblong, slightly toothed, varying in size up to 220 x 25mm. Flower-heads narrow, 7mm long; florets white, tinged blue. Each seed with a pappus of whitish hairs.

Flowers March – June.

106A

◄   *Phyla nodiflora*

▼

106B

107

Aster squamatus

COMPOSITAE

*108*A

▲

◄ *Atractylis flava*

*108*C

*108*B

Atractylis flava Seed-head

Atractylis flava Desf.   Ed. Herb. 39, 281, 347   *108*

Perennial or annual thistle-like herb, only 10 – 15cm high, quite common in gravelly *wadis* and various localities in the central depression, including the Jebel, as it well withstands dry harsh conditions. It has pale greyish slightly woolly stems and leaves; leaves leathery, dentate, with spinous teeth. There are spines on the involucre scales; the involucre surrounds the globe-shaped head, almost completely enclosing the cream florets. The seeds have tufts like cotton-wool.

Flowers April – May.

109 *Calendula aegyptiaca* Desf.   Ed. Herb. 250

An annual herb, c 8cm high, found in gravelly sand in the central depression after rain. Leaves flat, aromatic, 60 x 7mm. Flowers 8mm long; florets pale orange; central disc florets small, ray florets around edge of disc ligulate. The seed head consists of a ring of semicircular seeds without pappuses.

Flowers February, or after rain.

* *Calendula micrantha* Tineo & Guss.

Flowers orange, often with dark-coloured central disc florets.

B.N.H.S. 1987.

110 *Eclipta alba* (L.) L.   Ed. Herb. 272

Erect branching annual herb, up to 40cm tall, found in northern areas near irrigated fields and gardens. Stems reddish, shiny, with short stiff flat hairs. Leaves paired, dark green, lanceolate, 45 x 13mm. Solitary or paired flower-heads on peduncles are 7.5mm long, surrounded by sharply pointed bracts; central florets pale green, tubular; rays white, ligules 2mm long. Seeds blackish, arrow-shaped, ridged, 2.5mm long, lacking pappuses.

Flowers April – June.

Calendula aegyptiaca

Eclipta alba

III

Filago cf *desertorum*

II2

Flaveria trinervia

Filago cf *desertorum* Pomel   Ed. Herb. 33/4   *III*

A tiny annual herb not more than 5cm high, common on compact
desert soil after rain, particularly in the Tree of Life* area.
Prostrate or procumbent branches radiate from the base; stems,
leaves and heads greyish, woolly or cottony. Flower-heads minute,
in clusters of about 12, with barely visible dull-yellow florets.
    Flowers February – April.
    Arabic name: '*Qottainah*'.

Filago spathulata Presl var. *prostrata* Parl.
    =*F. desertorum* Pomel
                                                        R.G. 1950.

Flaveria trinervia (Spr.) Mohr   Ed. Herb. 101   *II2*

Annual herb of moist habitats in date palm plantations, gardens
and fields. Leaves have 3 prominent parallel nerves on the
underside. Flower-heads are composed of bracts and minute
yellow florets and borne in dense spherical clusters in leaf-axils.
Achenes without pappuses.
    Flowers February.
    An introduced species from South America which has become a
serious weed in some regions.

*p.30

113 *Francoeuria crispa* (Forssk.) Cass.   Ed. Herb. 128, 306
A perennial plant with numerous slender tangled branches
forming dense clumps up to 20cm high, occurring frequently in
depressions on the backslopes and in the central depression, in
fine compact soil composed of sediments from run-off or
accumulated rainwater. Leaves greyish-green elliptical-linear,
wavy-margined, 5 – 8mm long, clasping and lying along stems.
Flower-heads deep yellow, discoid, 5mm across; usually with no
ligulate ray florets, but when present ligules are almost too small
to be seen. Each seed has a parachute of bristly brownish hairs.
   Flowers March – May, and through the year.
   Arabic name: '*Githgath*'.

114 *Pulicaria undulata* (L.) C.A. Mey.   Ed. Herb. 229, 305
Perennial shrublet with procumbent tangled stems, found in a
wadi east of Hamad Town. Very similar in appearance to
Francoeuria crispa. Leaves grey-green, crinkle-margined, 5 –
10mm long, clasping and close to stems; flower-heads discoid,
with ligulate ray florets 1 – 2mm long; seeds with a parachute of
hairs.
   Flowers February – May.

113^A

Francoeuria crispa ▶

113^B

114^A

Pulicaria undulata

114^B

115ᴬ

Pulicaria gnaphalodes ▶
▼

115ᴮ

115ᶜ

Pulicaria gnaphalodes

Pulicaria gnaphalodes (Vent.) Boiss.   Ed. Herb. 115, 195, 350   *115*

Perennial strongly aromatic herb, woody-based and with many
erect branches, up to 30cm high. It flourishes in gravelly *wadis* in
the central depression and backslopes. Stems and leaves pale
bluish-green, extremely woolly; leaves 10 – 20mm long with
undulating margins. Length of flower-head 8mm; only 10 – 12
dull yellow florets in each head. Each achene has a tuft of
brownish bristles in a cup and resembles a miniature shuttlecock.

Flowers April – June, and September.

A plant unpalatable to grazing animals and flourishing where
others are regularly grazed bare.

116 *Ifloga spicata* (Forssk.) Sch. Bip.   Ed. Herb. 18a/b

Commonly found in stony or gravelly sand among the gravemounds on the backslopes, on the lower Jebel slopes and in hollows in the central depression after rain, this small annual herb sometimes only reaches a height of 3cm, but is usually c 10cm tall. It has a few simple branches arising from its base; these are densely clothed with clusters of minute flower-heads between needlelike leaves; the flower-heads are surrounded by membranous bracts.

Flowers February – March.
Flower-spikes become attractive when dried off, after dispersing their seeds.

117 *Koelpinia linearis* Pall.   Ed. Herb. 4

An uncommon herb, slender and possessing few branches; up to 20cm high, found in *wadis* in the central depression. Leaves are linear. Flowers yellow but inconspicuous; florets not exceeding their surrounding involucre of bracts. The fruiting head of elongated curving spiny seeds is unusual and eye-catching; each seed is tipped with a tuft of tiny bristles.

Flowers February.

*   *Launaea capitata* (Spr.) Dandy

Stems 5 – 15cm high, almost leafless; leaves in basal rosette; heads at tips of stems densely clustered*.

B.N.H.S. 1987.

Launaea cassiniana*   D.B. 1979/81.

*See pp.216, 217

116

117

Ifloga spicata (Foreground *Bassia eriophora*)

Koelpinia linearis

COMPOSITAE

Launaea species

118

Launaea cf *cassiniana*

119A *Launaea* cf *nudicaulis*

119B *Launaea* cf *nudicaulis*

216

Launaea cf *cassiniana* (Jaub. & Spach) Burkill
    Ed. Herb. 232, 254   *118*

Annual herb, c 15cm high, found by roadsides and in *wadis* in the north, in gravelly sand. Its bright green somewhat fleshy leaves are dissected into fine lobes with dentate margins, and mostly clustered at the base of the plant. Flower-heads 10mm wide; florets bright yellow, all strap-shaped. Each achene with a pappus of short white silky hairs.
    Flowers February – March.
    Arabic name: '*Huwwah*', also applied to other similar plants.

Launaea cf *mucronata* (Forssk.) Muschler   Ed. Herb. 22   *

Erect annual herb up to 40cm high, sometimes with many branches, common in sandy soils in northern areas. Stems and leaves always moist to the touch. Leaves lobed, mucronate; large radical leaves rosetted at the base; cauline leaves smaller and with auricles. Florets yellow, all ligulate. Seeds with pappuses of soft white silky hairs.
    Flowers March – April.

Launaea mucronata (Forssk.) Muschler   R.G. 1950.

Launaea nudicaulis (L.) Hook.f.   Ed. Herb. 123, 233   *119*

Perennial herb, common in all habitats and types of soil, requiring scant amounts of moisture. Leaves forming a rosette at the base of the plant only; leaves deeply cut into lobes with toothed margins; reddish in dry conditions. Flowers in varying shades of yellow, 10mm across; florets ligulate, with the 5 teeth of the strap, representing the tips of five fused petals, clearly visible. Seeds with pappuses of soft white hairs formed into gossamer spheres.
    Flowers January – April.

Launaea procumbens (Roxb.) Ram. & Rajg.   *

Perennial slender procumbent herb of irrigated habitats. Leaves with triangular lobes, in a basal rosette; cauline leaves small. Flowers pale yellow, 8mm wide, florets ligulate. Seeds with pappus of white hairs.
                                      K.V. 1978/79.

* *Matricaria auriculata* (Boiss.) Muschler

An aromatic herb with finely dissected leaves and yellow conical flower-heads; ray florets not present.

R.G. 1950.

120 Pluchea ovalis (Pers.) DC.   Ed. Herb. 106

A shrub growing readily in moist habitats, particularly in the Adhari area, and reaching a height of 1.5m. It has many branches bearing broad aromatic leaves 40 – 80mm long; leaves auricled and dentate-margined, each tooth furnished with a minute prickle. Flower-heads 5mm long, in corymbose clusters; florets pinkish. Pappuses of soft hairs aid dispersal of seeds.

Flowers February – March.

120A

Pluchea ovalis

120B

Pluchea ovalis

*121*A

Reichardia species

*121*B

Reichardia species with seed-heads

Reichardia species   *121*

Compact annual herb, only a few cm high, common on the
northern backslope and adjacent areas. It has a basal rosette of
leaves; leaves may be deeply lobed or not. Flower-heads large and
borne on thick stems; the pale-margined scales of the involucre
are distinctive; florets brilliant yellow, all strap-shaped, often
with dark-coloured centres. Pappus of dense fine white hairs
attached to each seed*.
   Flowers February – April.
   Arabic name: '*Huwwah*'.

Reichardia tingitana (L.) Roth   D.B. 1979/81.

Rhanterium epapposum Oliv.   Ed. Herb. 164   *

Small shrub with slender smooth whitish-grey woody branches,
only seen on the south-west backslope within Al Areen Wildlife
Park. Habitat, stony gravelly *wadi* overlaid by wind-borne sand.
C 50cm tall, more when not browsed. Pale green narrow leaves,
dentate-margined with few teeth, c 15mm long, arise alternately
and quite widely spaced along stems. Flower-heads solitary, 7mm
wide, at stem tips, composed of slightly shaggy spherical bundles
of bright yellow florets subtended by rows of pointed bracts;
florets strap-shaped, ligule 2 – 3mm long. There is no pappus on
the seed.
   Flowers April – June.
   Arabic name: '*Arfaj*'.
   Widely recognised and exploited as a valuable food plant for
animals and source of firewood, which explains its scarcity on
Bahrain.

*Illustration p.34

COMPOSITAE

122 *Scolymus maculatus* L.   Ed. Herb. 308

Thistle plant, 50cm high, found growing as a weed by a newly
planted palm beside the dirt road between Isa Town and Aali.
Stem white with few lateral branches. Leaves spiny, green, with
prominently white midrib and veins, deeply lobed nearly to the
midrib, decurrent, continuing down the stem to form wings each
side. Flower-head 25mm long; involucre of green scales
surrounds and nips in golden-yellow florets, which exceed it by
5mm.

Flowers April – May.
English name: 'Golden Thistle'.

123 *Senecio* cf *glaucus* L.   Ed. Herb. 20

Annual herb whose bright yellow flowers provide welcome
patches of colour along roadsides and in desert areas after rain.
Height up to 15cm. Leaves slightly fleshy, 20 – 30mm long,
divided into a few well-spaced linear lobes with slightly toothed
margins. Flower-heads are carried at tips of stalks of different
lengths in corymbose formation, presenting a level mass of
flowers; heads 6 – 10mm wide, with tubular disc florets ringed by
strap-shaped rays. Seeds with a parachute of fine silky hairs are
swiftly carried away by the wind.

Flowers March – April.
Relative of 'Groundsel' and 'Ragwort'. A true ephemeral,
appearing just after rain, swiftly flowering and producing seeds
then vanishing again within a short space of time.
Senecio species recorded Hawar island group C.C. 1983.

*   *Senecio coronopifolius* Desf.
    =*S. desfontainei* Druce   R.G. 1950.

222

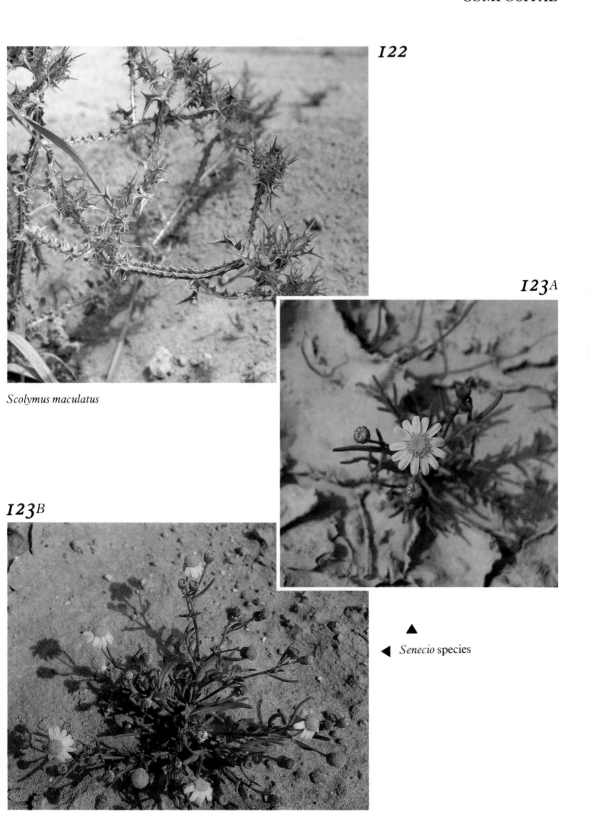

I22

Scolymus maculatus

I23A

I23B

▲
◀ *Senecio* species

COMPOSITAE

124A

124B

▲

Sonchus asper ▶

125A   *Sonchus oleraceus*

125B   *Sonchus oleraceus* Seed-head

Sonchus asper(L.) Hill subsp. *asper*   Ed. Herb.260   *124*

Robust annual herb; a tenacious weed in gardens and fields where
the soil has been worked and moisture is available. It has
deep green leaves with prickly margins and rounded auricles;
leaves may be tinged red in dry conditions. The plant produces
just a few branches, each bearing several flower-heads on small
stalks at its tip; heads composed of yellow ligulate florets and up
to 15mm long. Seeds with pappus of long white hairs.
   Flowers March – April.

Sonchus oleraceus (L.) Gouan   Ed. Herb. 261   *125*

Common and widespread weed of cultivated land, a robust erect
herb with few branches. Leaves large, bright green, with
dentate-margined triangular lobes and pointed auricles.
Flower-heads up to 15mm long, with yellow strap-shaped florets.
Pappuses of long white silky hairs.
   Flowers March – April.
   Arabic name: '*Aadheed*'.
   English name: 'Smooth Sow-thistle'.
   Plants which, in common with their relative the 'dandelion',
   contain milky sap believed to possess magical properties. The
   leaves are edible and may be cooked or eaten raw in salads.

Urospermum picroides L.   ✳

Large heads with yellow ligulate florets and involucral bracts in
one row.

                                                      R.G. 1950.

Vicoa pentanema Aitch. & Hemsl.   ✳

Flower-heads composed of minute yellow florets within
globe-shaped woolly involucres.

                                                      R.G. 1950.

LILIOPSIDA (Monocotyledons)

HYDROCHARITACEAE (Frog-bit Family)

Submerged marine plants with linear leaves and minute flowers
arranged in spathes of 1 or 2 bracts.

 126

Halophila stipulacea
R.G. 1950.

*   *Halophila ovalis* (R. Br.) Hook.f.

126 *Halophila stipulacea* (Forssk.) Asch.   Ed. Herb. 314

NAJADACEAE

Herbaceous marine plants with linear leaves and simple flowers.

127

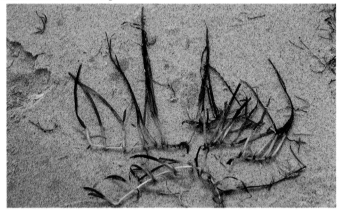

Halodule wrightii

127 *Halodule wrightii* Asch.   Ed. Herb. 315

POTAMOGETONACEAE (Pondweed Family)

Aquatic submerged herbs with inflorescence often projecting as a
spike above the water surface.

*   *Diplanthera uninervis* (Forssk.) Asch.   R.G. 1950.

*   *Potamogeton* species aff. *pusillus*   R.G. 1950.

LILIACEAE (Lily Family)

Herbs with leaves from the base; flowers, with 3 sepals resembling petals and 3 petals, arranged in racemes; fruit a 3-chambered capsule.

Dipcadi erythraeum Webb & Berth.   *128*

Rare on Bahrain is this lily, and well worth searching for, as it possesses beautiful flowers of an unusual colour. The plant can be found on rocky outcrops south of the Jebel in stony sand. 2 dark green linear leaves and a raceme of brown bell-shaped flowers stem from an underground bulb. Each corolla is 10mm long with a tube extending into 3 outer and 3 inner lobes. The fruit is a large capsule with 3 chambers.

Flowers February.

128

Dipcadi erythraeum

129B

129C

Asphodelus fistulosus Flowers ▲

◀ Fruit

Asphodelus fistulosus L.   Ed. Herb. 5a/b, 166, 239   **129**
    =*A. tenuifolius* Cav.

A delicate lily, 10 – 50cm high, carpeting depressions, *wadis* and roadsides in desert areas after rain*. It has bright green stems, occasionally branched, and numerous grass-like leaves arising from its base. Flowers 5mm long, in racemes; each white petal with a dark purple central vein. Seeds in a 3-valved capsule. The plant has short fibrous roots, not a bulb as might be expected.

Flowers February – March, later if rains are scant or late.
Vernacular name: '*Burwaq*' or 'Little Onion'.
Gathered for use as a potherb.
Recorded Jazirat Hawar C.C. 1983.

129A

Asphodelus fistulosus

Asphodelus viscidulus Boiss.

R.G. 1950.   *

*pp.19, 20 and illustration p.29

JUNCACEAE (Rush Family)
Grass-like herbs with unbranched stems and cylindrical leaves.
Flowers are clustered in cymes; perianth 6-partite with 6 stamens.
Fruit a many-seeded capsule.

I30 *Juncus rigidus* Desf.   Ed. Herb. 184, 279
Perennial rush with rigidly erect bright green stems and tough
needle-sharp leaves, found on damp or marshy open ground to
the north and east of Aali, by the shore at Jasra and along ditches;
occurs with *Aeluropus* species. The plants arise from rhizomes
forming closely packed straight rows. Flower-stems twice the
height of leaves, up to 1.5m tall; flowers brownish, with dark red
stamens. Fruit shiny, reddish-brown, elliptical, 4mm long, with
many minute seeds.
   Flowers April.
   Vernacular name: 'Asal'.
   A halophytic plant tolerating well the high salinity of the soil in
   its habitats.

*   *Juncus acutus* var. *maritimus* L.   R.G. 1950.

*   *Juncus maritimus* L.   R.G. 1950.

CYPERACEAE (Sedge Family)
Grass-like herbs with solid, often 3-sided, stems. Leaves linear
with a sheath at the base enclosing the stem. Flowers clustered on
small spikes; each simple flower subtended by a glume, enclosing
an ovary, 2 – 3 stamens and 2 – 3 stigmas. Fruit is a lens-shaped
or 3-sided grain-like achene.

I3I *Cyperus laevigatus* L.   Ed. Herb. 328
      =*Juncellus laevigatus* L.
Bright green tussocks, 60cm tall, along stream-banks in northern
areas. Leaves stiff, short with a long sheath at the base.
Flower-stems terete, each bearing a cluster of 6 – 7
many-flowered spikelets just below the tip. Flowers green-pale
brown, spikelet 10mm long.
   Flowers March – May.

130A *Juncus rigidus*

130B *Juncus rigidus*

131

Cyperus laevigatus

132A

Cyperus conglomeratus ▶

132C

132B

Cyperus conglomeratus

132D

Cyperus arenarius Retz.   ✳
                        R.G. 1950, K.V. 1978/79.

Cyperus conglomeratus Rottb.   Ed. Herb. 3, 69, 104, 140, 253   *I32*

Common perennial sedge, 12 – 60cm tall, spreading by rhizomes and forming tussocks, in most habitats, particularly those adjacent to sea-shores with deep coarse sand. Base of stems reddish-brown and ragged; roots encased in sand which adheres to them forming a protective layer. Leaves stiff, grooved, curving. Flowers in dense pointed spikelets arranged in clusters, tightly in heads or openly branched on stalks; flower-heads brown, occasionally green.

Flowers April – June.

Arabic name: '*Qassis*'.

Possibly several varieties of this species are present on Bahrain as it varies in form considerably.

New shoots soon line desert *wadis* and depressions with a fuzz of green after rain or heavy dew. The plants are severely cropped by grazing animals in several localities.

133 *Cyperus rotundus* L.   Ed. Herb. 288

Perennial grass-like weed of moist habitats, c 15cm high. Stems and leaves bright green, leaves shiny, with a keel or ridge. Inflorescence of brownish spikelets arranged in branching heads.

Flowers April.

Arabic name: '*Se'd*'.

*   *Fimbristylis ferruginea* Vahl   R.G. 1950.

133   *Cyperus rotundus*

GRAMINEAE (Poaceae, Grass Family)

Annual or perennial green herbs with many strap-shaped linear leaves and long slender jointed culms, hollow between nodes, bearing panicles or spikes of flowers; stolons and/or rhizomes present. Leaves arise from base of plants or along stems, each leaf forming a long split sheath around the stem below the point at which stem and leaf meet. Inside the leaf-blade, at this junction, is the *ligule*, a ring of hairs or membranous tissue often in the form of a flap. Basic flower unit a *floret*, comprising an ovary, 2 stigmas and, often, 3 stamens, usually enclosed by 2 minute bracts, the *palea* and *lemma*; coloured anthers and feathery stigmas often plainly visible; some plants with separate male and female florets. 1 or more florets on a central stem, subtended by 2 bracts, *glumes*, form a *spikelet*; spikelets arranged in clusters or on fine stalks. It is common for the lemma or glume to possess an *awn*. Fruit a caryopsis or grain.

In favourable habitats with moist loamy soil and in hollows or *wadis* where water accumulates, grasses form a mat-like covering; in dry desert areas the plants grow in well-spaced tussocks*.

Although individually inconspicuous, grass flowers are arranged in inflorescences of fascinating variety.

About 36 species from the huge grass family have been recorded on Bahrain.

*p.19

DESERT GRASSES

134A

Stipagrostis plumosa ▶

▼

134B

134

Stipagrostis plumosa
   (L.) Munro
   Ed. Herb. 223, 357
Height c 30cm; culm with several
nodes. Leaves rolled, flexuous,
60mm long*; ligule of long hairs.
Panicle 120mm long; awn has a
central plume with 2 lateral
branches; tip of plume pointed.

135

Stipagrostis socotrana

Stipagrostis socotrana (Vierh.) de Winter   Ed. Herb. 103, 360   *135*
Height c 15cm; culm angled, single-noded. Leaves short, rolled,
20mm long*; ligule of short hairs. Panicle 80mm long; awn with
central plume and 2 lateral branches; tip of plume obtuse.

*p.19

136A

136 *Cymbopogon* species
 Ed. Herb. 174
 Height to 50cm; each pair of
 flower-spikes surrounded by
 a boat-shaped spathe.

Cymbopogon schoenanthus (L.) Spr.

136B

▲

Cymbopogon species ▶

R.G. 1950.

137

◀ *Dichanthium annulatum* ▲   *137A*

Dichanthium annulatum
 (Forssk.) Stapf (Det.Au.) Ed. Herb. 289
Large dense tussocks up to 75cm
tall, in northern *wadi*.

Dichanthium annulatum (Forssk.) Desf.   R.G. 1950.

 B.N.H.S. 1987.

137B

*   *Cutandia dichotoma* (Forssk.) Trabut   R.G. 1950.

*   *Cutandia memphitica* (Spr.) Benth.

138

Eremopogon foveolatus

139   *Hyparrhenia hirta*

Eremopogon foveolatus   (Del.) Stapf (Pr. Det.)   *138*
  =*Dicanthium foveolatum*
  (Del.) Roberty   Ed. Herb. 72, 173
Height to 40cm; leaves linear, grooved, nodes
reddish with hairs; spikes slender, silky,
with awns 15 – 20mm long.

Hyparrhenia hirta   (L.) Stapf (Pr. Det.)   *139*
  Ed. Herb. 201, 222
Height c 40cm; stems and leaves bright pale
green, leaves curling, rolled; spikes with
reddish-brown spathes.

140

Stipa capensis

Stipa capensis Thunb. (Pr. Det.)   Ed. Herb. 75, 244   *140*

*141*A

Panicum turgidum

*141*B

141 *Panicum turgidum* Forssk.   Ed. Herb. 71, 268
Tangled clumps, up to 60cm tall; nodes angled;
white feathery stigmas and vermilion anthers.
Fodder grass.

Panicum turgidum

*142*A

Pennisetum divisum

142 *Pennisetum divisum* (Gmelin) Henrard
Ed. Herb. 228, 252, 269
Height 60 – 80cm; awns stiff, long, pale-purplish;
anthers orange.

* 	*Tricholaena teneriffae* (L.) Pall.
=*Panicum teneriffae* R. Br.

Pennisetum divisum   *142*B

R.G.1950.

Chrysopogon species   Ed. Herb. 270   *

Tussocks with stiff pale green erect culms. Panicles
golden-bearded; spikelets in groups of three, each group with 5
plumose awns.
    Growing among rocks on the Jebel.

Eleusine compressa in a sandy gully
at the foot of the Jebel

144A   Tetrapogon villosus

Eleusine compressa (Forssk.) Asch. & Schweinf.   *143*
R.G. 1950.

144B   Tetrapogon villosus

Tetrapogon villosus Desf. (Pr. Det.)   Ed. Herb. 73, 277   *144*
Flower-spike soft, purplish, 40 – 60mm x 15mm; spikelets
villous*.
    Grows in sandy hollows between rocks on the Jebel.

    *Illustration p.40

SABKHA GRASSES

145

145 *Aeluropus lagopoides*
(L.) Trin. ex Thwaites
Ed. Herb. 329, 337
Height to 20cm; leaves
10 – 30mm x 2 – 3mm; heads
10 – 12mm long.
Vernacular name: 'Aqrish'.

Aeluropus lagopoides

146B   *Sporobolus arabicus*

Sporobolus arabicus

146A

146 *Sporobolus arabicus* Boiss.   Ed. Herb. 105, 245
Height c 60cm. Panicle 100 – 150mm long.

SWAMP GRASSES

147A

Aeluropus littoralis

Aeluropus littoralis (Gouan) Parl.   Ed. Herb. 333   **147**

Inflorescence of usually 6 flower-spikes, each 10mm long, on alternate sides of stem; spikelets in double rows.

Thickly covers wide areas between mangroves.

147B

147C   *Aeluropus littoralis*

148
Imperata cylindrica

148 *Imperata cylindrica* (L.) P. Beauv.
Ed. Herb. 133
Height c 1m; inflorescence a
dense silky spike-like panicle.

149 *Paspalum vaginatum* Sw.
(Pr. Det.)   Ed. Herb. 364
Height c 50cm; flower-spikes
paired, 40mm long.
Vernacular name: '*Murrani*'

149   *Paspalum vaginatum*

*150*A

▼ *Phragmites australis* ▲

*150*B

Phragmites australis (Cav.) Trin. ex Steud.   Ed. Herb. 321,   *150*
    332, 354

=*P. communis* Trin.

Height to 2.5m; leaves 70 – 500mm x 8 – 20mm; ligule a ring of
hairs.

Grows in saline silty loamy soils with high water-table.

Vernacular name: '*Gassab*' or '*Gasba*'.

Phragmites communis Trin. var. *stenophylla*   *

R.G. 1950.

245

GRASSES OF IRRIGATED LAND

151

Chloris gayana

152

Cynodon dactylon

151 *Chloris gayana* Kunth (Pr. Det.)
   Ed. Herb. 296, 297
   Height up to 90cm; flower-spikes
   70 – 100mm long.
      Vernacular name: '*Negl*'.

152 *Cynodon dactylon* (L.) Pers. (Pr. Det.)   Ed. Herb. 74, 266
   Creeping grass with long stolons. Leaves 4mm wide; ligule a ring
   with hairs. Digitate inflorescence of 3 – 5, usually 4, spikes about
   50mm long.
      Vernacular name: '*Nejma*' or '*Negl*'.

153ᴬ
Dactyloctenium
aegyptium

Dactyloctenium aegyptium (L.) Willd.   Ed. Herb. 70, 178   *153*
Leaves 7mm broad; digitate flower-spikes 20mm x 6mm.

153ᴮ
Dactyloctenium aegyptium

154A

Polypogon monspeliensis

154B

154 *Polypogon monspeliensis*
      (L.) Desf.
      Ed. Herb. 132, 284
      Height to 40cm; culms angled
      with swollen joints; leaves soft,
      10mm wide. Flower-spikes soft,
      silvery, up to 100mm x 25mm.

Polypogon monspeliensis

*   *Phalaris minor* Retz.

R.G. 1950.

155ᴬ

▲

◀ *Setaria verticillata*

Setaria verticillata (L.) P. Beauv.   *155*
    Ed. Herb. 179
Height c 30cm; leaves bright
green, soft, c 10mm wide.
Flower-spike 30 – 50mm long;
spikelets surrounded by barbed
bristles.

155ᴮ   *Cenchrus echinatus* L.   ✱

                                              B.N.H.S. 1987.

        Koeleria phleoides (Vill.) Pers.   ✱
            =*Rostraria cristata* (L.) Tzvelev   R.G. 1950.

157 *Echinochloa colona*

158 *Lolium perenne*

156

Panicum species

156 *Panicum* species   Ed. Herb. 283

157 *Echinochloa colona* (L.) Link
    Ed. Herb. 286
    Height c 40cm; leaves broad,
    soft; flower-spikes oblong, 15mm
    long.

158 *Lolium perenne* L. (Pr. Det.)
    Ed. Herb. 287
    Height 50cm; leaves tapering,
    shiny; spikelets 12mm long.

*   *Brachypodium distachyon* (L.) P. Beauv.
      =*Trachynia distachya* (L.) Link   R.G. 1950.

*   *Panicum maximum*   K.V. 1978/79.

*   *Sphenopus divaricatus* (Gouan) Reichb.   R.G. 1950.

159

Schismus barbatus

Schismus barbatus (L.) Thell.   *159*

R.G. 1950, K.V. 1978/79.

160

Sporobolus spicatus

Sporobolus spicatus (Vahl) Kunth   Ed. Herb. 344   *160*

K.V. 1978/79.

Cenchrus ciliaris L.   *

R.G. 1950.

PALMAE (Arecaceae, Palm Family)
Woody plants with thick unbranched stem and suckers at the base; leaves tough, feather-like; flower-clusters in woody spathes; fruit a drupe.

_161_ *Phoenix dactylifera* L.   Ed. Herb. 182

Tall tree-like plant, up to 10m high, with woody stem. A cluster of long swaying pinnate leaves with numerous pairs of greyish-green leaflets arises around the top of the stem, creating a rounded feathery crown; as the stem grows and elongates, producing new leaves at its apex, old leaves droop and dry off but remain attached by their fibrous sheathing stems for some time*. Dioecious species, with both male and female trees producing large showy panicles crowded with flowers; the panicles emerge from woody spathes, the air becomes heavy with their distinctive perfume and clouds of pollen are released. Central flower-stalk thick, woody; flowers creamy-white, waxy; male flowers with 3 petals and 6 stamens; globose female flower with 3 carpels, one developing into a fruit. Fruit an oblong drupe comprising 1 seed in a hard casing surrounded by a layer of soft juicy flesh.

    Flowers February – March, fruit July – September.

    Vernacular name: '*Nakhl*'.

    English name: 'Date Palm'.

    Most 'date palms' on Bahrain are cultivated, in gardens or plantations as they have been for thousands of years, for their nutritious fruit and many other uses, but there are a number growing freely in small stands where the water-table is high, or close by irrigated land, chiefly in the north of the island. Scattered individuals appear in all parts of the desert however, particularly in sandy *wadis* or hollows.

*See p.25

161A

Phoenix dactylifera

Female flowers ▶

Male flowers
▼

161B

Phoenix dactylifera
Below left: Male flowers
Below right: Bearing fruit

161C

161D

Cultivated *Phoenix dactylifera*

161E Male flowers tied in with female flowers

161F Female flowers after pollination

161G Cultivated *Phoenix dactylifera* bearing fruit

*Gardeners carefully chop the old leaves from cultivated palms each year to aid growth and provide material for fences, screens, baskets and mats.

As the flowers develop during February they remove the woody flower-spathes early and tie bunches of male flowers (utilising strands of tough leaf-stem fibres) in among flower-clusters on female trees to ensure pollination for a good crop of fruit; this partly obviates the need for pollen trees so that plantations can be mostly stocked with fruit-bearing trees. Male flowers are sold in the *suq*. Young females can be easily selected from suckers around female 'parents'.

Natural palms rely on wind or insects, chiefly bees, for pollination.

Precis orythya butterflies flutter beneath date palms during late September and October and feed on their fallen sugary fruit.

162 TYPHACEAE (Cat-tail Family)

Tall grass-like marsh herbs with linear leaves; flowers densely crowded on cylindrical spikes; fruit minute, single-seeded.

Typha domingensis Pers. (Det.Au.)   Ed. Herb. 206

Reed grass, with stout stems up to 3m tall, growing in marshy places and spreading by rhizomes. Recorded on Bahrain in one locality only; east of Hamad Town in a *wadi* kept moist by periodic discharge from a sewage treatment station. Strap-shaped leaves up to 2.5m long and 15mm broad, with spongy centre; surface on one side of leaf convex; leaf-bases neatly sheathing stem from either side forming a thick knot at base of plant. Flowers borne on a terminal spike up to 50cm long; female and male separated; male flowers along the tip and female flowers massed into a thick cylinder below them. As the fruits develop this becomes pale brown and velvety; each minute seed is surrounded by the fine fluffy hairs on the ovary stalk.

Flowers April.

Forms dense stands with *Phragmites australis.*

162

Typha domingensis

IV

Glossary
Abbreviations
Bibliography and References
Index of Plant Names

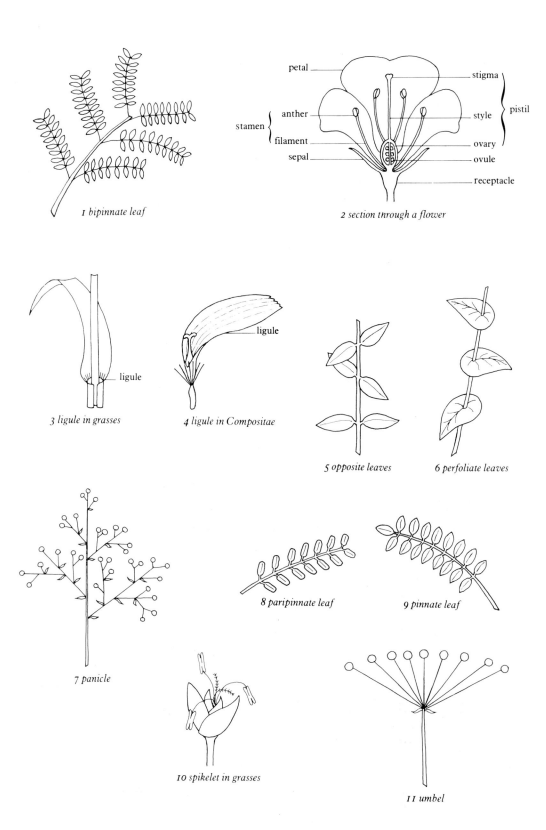

1 bipinnate leaf

petal ———————— ———— stigma

stamen { anther ———————— ———— style } pistil

filament ———————— ———— ovary

sepal ———————— ———— ovule

———————— receptacle

2 section through a flower

ligule

3 ligule in grasses

ligule

4 ligule in Compositae

5 opposite leaves

6 perfoliate leaves

7 panicle

8 paripinnate leaf

9 pinnate leaf

10 spikelet in grasses

11 umbel

Glossary

12 *alternate leaves*

achene	A simple one-seeded dry indehiscent fruit.
adventitious	Of roots, shoots etc. that arise in unexpected positions.
aeolian	Deposited by wind.
alfalfa	A fodder plant, *Medicago sativa*; lucerne.
alluvial	Of sand, mud etc. deposits formed by flowing water.
alternate*	A form of leaf arrangement in which there is one leaf at each node.
angiosperm	A plant bearing seeds enclosed within an ovary.
annual	A plant that completes its life cycle within a single year.
anther	The sac-like part at the tip of a stamen containing pollen (see diagram 2).
apex	The tip of an organ.
auricle	An ear-like projection from the base of a leaf.
awn	A bristle-like part, usually at the tip of an organ.
axil	The angle between the upper side of a leaf and the stem from which it grows.
axillary	Growing in an axil.
axis	Central part (stem etc.) around which organs (leaves, flowers etc.) develop.
barr	General Arabic term for the Bahrain desert areas.
berry	A fleshy fruit, usually with several seeds.
bilabiate	Two-lipped.
bilateral symmetry	In a flower that can be divided into two equal halves by only one line.
bipinnate*	A pinnate leaf with the divisions also pinnate.
bisexual	Having both male and female reproductive parts in the same flower.
bract	Small scale-like or leaf-like structure growing at the base of a flower or flower-head.
bracteate	With bracts.
bracteole	Minute bract.
calyx	Collective term for the sepals of a flower, usually green (see diagram 2).
canescent	Grey, silvery; hoary.
capitate	Having a globular head.
capitulum* (pl. capitula)	An inflorescence consisting of a head of small closely packed stalkless flowers, typical of Compositae.
capsule	A dry dehiscent fruit derived from two or more carpels.
carpel	A unit of the female part of a flower, usually comprising an ovary, style and stigma.
caryopsis	A one-seeded grain-like fruit (typical of grasses).
catkin	A pendulous inflorescence comprising a loose spike of numerous small stalkless flowers.
cauline	Borne on the stem (especially leaves); not radical.
chlorophyll	The green colouring substance in plants; it absorbs light energy in photosynthesis.
cleft	Of a leaf; deeply cut but not to the midrib.
cone	A more or less conical structure composed of bracts or scales enclosing simple male or female reproductive parts.
cordate*	Heart-shaped.
corolla	Collective term for the petals of a flower.
corymb*	An inflorescence in which the flowers are borne on lateral stalks of different lengths, the lower stalks being longest to form a flat-topped cluster.
crenate	Of a leaf with rounded marginal teeth.
culm	The stem of grasses or sedges.
cuticle	A thin covering on the aerial parts of plants.
cyathium (pl. cyathia)	A cup-shaped type of inflorescence as in Euphorbiaceae.
cyme	An inflorescence with all branches of limited growth; new growth is from the axils; older flowers are usually found at the apex of the stem.

13 *capitulum*

14 *cordate leaf*

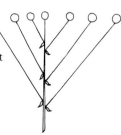

15 *corymb*

* See diagram

16 decussate leaves

17 deltoid leaf

18 elliptical leaf

19 lanceolate leaf

decumbent	Lying on the ground but with tips of branches or main stem ascending.
decurrent	Of leaf bases that fuse with and extend down the stem forming wings.
decussate*	Of opposite leaves with each pair at right angles to the one above.
deflexed	Bent sharply downwards.
dehiscent	Of fruit which stay on the plant and split open to release seeds.
deltoid*	Triangular.
dentate	Toothed; a notched leaf margin.
dichotomous	Divided, or dividing into two parts.
dicotyledons	The flowering plants having embryos with two cotyledons.
digitate	Of a compound leaf with leaflets arising from one point and spreading like the fingers of a hand.
dioecious	Having male and female on separate, distinct individual plants.
disc	The central portion of a flower-head in Compositae composed of tubular florets.
dominant	Of the most abundant plant species in a community.
drupe	A fleshy indehiscent fruit in which the seed or seeds have a hard covering.
elliptical*	Oval but narrowed acutely at each end.
entire	Describing a leaf without notches or indentations.
ephemeral	Plant with a short life cycle that can be completed during favourable conditions following rain.
epicalyx	A calyx-like structure outside the true calyx.
filament	The stalk-like part of a stamen supporting the anther (see diagram 2).
filiform	Threadlike.
flexuous	Full of curves; bending.
floret	A small flower as in the Compositae or grasses.
flower*	The reproductive unit of a flowering plant; a structure comprising sepals, petals, stamens and carpels.
follicle	A dry dehiscent fruit developed from a single ovary, opening along one line.
fruit	The ripened ovary, often with attached parts.
genus **(pl. genera)**	An important rank in the taxonomic grouping of plants, below family and above the rank of species; the genus is the first part of the scientific name of a species.
glabrous	Smooth, not hairy.
gland	A secreting organ or structure, usually on or near the plant surface.
globose	Round; spherical, or almost so.
glume	One of a pair of bracts below each spikelet in a grass inflorescence (see diagram 10).
gymnosperm	A plant with seeds exposed, not enclosed in an ovary.
gypsic	Chalky from the presence of gypsum – hydrated Calcium sulphate.
halophyte	A plant adapted to live in soil containing a high concentration of salt.
haustorium **(pl. haustoria)**	A sucker by which a parasitic plant extracts nutrients from its host.
hawaj	Arabic term for a herbalist.
head	A crowded cluster of stalked or unstalked flowers, as in the Compositae.
herb	A soft, usually green plant; non-woody.
hispid	Covered with coarse or stiff hairs.
indehiscent	Describing a fruit that does not open to disperse seeds; the whole fruit falls from the plant.
inflexed	Bent or folded inwards.
inflorescence	The arrangement of flowers on a plant.
involucre	The whorl of bracts enclosing a flower-head or cluster as in Compositae or Umbelliferae.
irregular	A flower with petals that are not uniform in shape.
labiate	Lipped; of flowers as in Labiatae.
laciniate	Jagged; cut into narrow irregular lobes.
lanceolate*	Shaped like a lance; narrow and tapering towards the tip.
lateral	On or from the side of an organ.
legume	A pod; a dry dehiscent fruit containing one or more seeds, developed from a single carpel and usually opening along two lines.

* See diagram

lemma	The lower bract beneath a grass flower (of a pair; the other being the palea). (See diagram 10)
ligulate	Strap-shaped.
ligule*	i) A thin membranous outgrowth at the top of the leaf-sheath in grasses; a scale-like flap or often a ring of hairs.
	ii) A strap-shaped corolla, often of ray florets in Compositae; the five teeth of the ligule representing the tips of five fused petals.

20 obcordate leaf

limb	The upper spreading part of a corolla or calyx.
linear	Slender, narrow.
littoral	Of the seashore between low and high tide lines.
lobe	A roundish projection or division.
lobed	Describing a leaf that is divided but with an undivided central area.
local	Restricted to a particular place.
locule	A cavity or compartment.
marsh	A tract of low wet land where the water table is at or just beneath the soil surface.

21 oblong leaf

mealy	With pale flecks as if covered with powder.
mesophyte	A plant without adaptations to environmental extremes.
mono-cotyledons	The flowering plants having embryos with one cotyledon (seed leaf).
monoecious	Having both male and female flowers on the same plant.
mucronate	Abruptly tipped with a small fine point.
node	A point on the stem from which one or more leaves arise.
nutlet	Hard one-seeded portions into which certain fruits divide at maturity.
obcordate*	Reversed heart-shaped.
oblong*	Longer than broad.

22 obovate leaf

obovate/obovoid*	Reversed egg-shaped.
obtuse	Blunt; not acute.
opposite*	A form of leaf arrangement in which a pair of leaves occur at each node with one leaf on either side of the stem.
orbicular*	Rounded; circular.
ovate*	Egg-shaped; pointed at the tip and usually broader near the base.
ovule	The structure containing the female reproductive cell which after fertilization develops into a seed (see diagram 2).
palea	The upper bract of a pair beneath a grass flower (the other being the lemma). (See diagram 10)
palmate*	Lobed or divided into more than three leaflets arising from a single point; spreading like the fingers of a hand.
panicle*	A branching inflorescence.

23 orbicular leaf

papilionate/papilionaceous	Having an irregular corolla, shaped something like a butterfly as in Leguminosae.
papilla (pl. papillae)	Small elongated projection.
pappillose	Having papillae; warty.
pappus	A modified calyx consisting of a ring of hair-like lobes, scales etc.
parasite	A species obtaining food at the expense of another, the host.
paripinnate*	Evenly pinnate with all the leaflets paired.
pedicel	The stalk of a single flower.
peduncle	The main axis or stalk of an inflorescence.
perennial	Having a life-cycle that lasts for more than two years.
perfoliate*	Of sessile leaves in which the leaf base completely encircles the stem of the plant.
perianth	In a flower the calyx and corolla or the outer whorl protecting the developing reproductive parts (see diagram 2).
petal	One of the flower-parts immediately inside the sepals; often brightly coloured (see diagram 2).
petiole	A leaf-stalk.

24 ovate leaf

25 palmate leaf

* See diagram

GLOSSARY

26 pinnatifid leaf

27 raceme

28 rhomboidal leaf

29 sagittate leaf

30 spathulate leaf

photosynthesis	The process by which plants use sunlight in the production of carbohydrates from water, carbon dioxide and inorganic salts.
pinna	One of the primary leaflets in a pinnate leaf.
pinnate*	Describing a compound leaf with leaflets arranged along either side of a common central stalk.
pinnatifid/ pinnatisect*	Deeply cut into lobes but not to the midrib.
pistil	The female reproductive organ of a flower consisting of stigma, style and ovary (see diagram 2).
pneumato- phore	A breathing root that protrudes above soil level.
pollen(grains)	Microspores containing the male cells for reproduction.
procumbent	Trailing or lying loosely on the ground.
propagation	Reproduction by natural processes.
prostrate	Lying flat on the ground.
pubescent	Covered with short fine soft hairs.
raceme*	An unbranched inflorescence with pedicelled flowers along the main stem; older flowers are at the bottom and youngest at the apex.
radical	Growing from the root; basal (rosetted) leaves.
rays	The strap-shaped florets in members of the Compositae; see *ligule*.
receptacle	The expanded part at the end of a flower-stalk to which the floral parts are attached (see diagram 2).
recurvate	Curving or bending backwards.
reflexed	Bent sharply backwards.
revolute	Rolled downwards or backwards.
rhizome	A horizontal underground stem which by producing shoots and roots acts as an agent of vegetative propagation.
rhomboidal*	Diamond-shaped.
rootstock	Basal persistent part of stem of herbaceous perennial from which new shoots arise after dormant season.
rosette	Circular cluster of radical leaves.
ruderal	Growing near human habitations in waste places.
sabkha	Arabic term for salt flats with fine-textured saline soil, sometimes hard-packed or with salt crust and usually with high saline water table.
sagittate*	Shaped like an arrow-head.
scape	A leafless peduncle bearing one or many flowers.
scarious	Thin, dry, membranous.
seed	A structure containing an embryo plant and a food store that develops from a fertilized ovule.
sepal	A leaf-like unit of the calyx, the outer whorl of perianth segments, usually green but sometimes coloured and resembling petals (see diagram 2).
serrate	Saw-toothed.
sessile	Without a stalk.
shrub	A woody perennial plant, smaller than a tree, with several branches from the base.
silicle (*silicula*)	A dry dehiscent fruit similar to a silique except that it is as broad or broader than it is long.
silique (*siliqua*)	An elongated pod-like dry dehiscent fruit derived from two carpels, in Cruciferae.
simple	Not divided into parts; not compound.
solitary	Describes an inflorescence consisting of a single flower.
spadix	A succulent spike with tiny densely-packed flowers.
spathe	A large bract enclosing an inflorescence.
spathulate*	Spatula-shaped; having a broad apex and long narrow base.
spermato- phyte	Seed plant; a plant in the division containing seed-bearing plants.

* See diagram

spike*	An elongated inflorescence in which the flowers are sessile round a central stalk.
spikelet*	The basic unit in a grass inflorescence, usually of one or more florets and their bracts.
spine	A modified leaf or part of a leaf forming a sharp-pointed projection.
stamen	The pollen-bearing male reproductive organ of a flower (see diagram 2).
staminode	A sterile, often reduced, stamen.
stellate	In star-shaped formation.
stipule	Scale-like or leaf-like appendage at the leaf-base or along the leaf-stalk.
stolon	A long stem reaching to the ground with new plants growing from nodes which contact the soil.
subtend	To enclose in its axil; applied to a leaf or bract.
succulent	Swollen and fleshy with stored water; a plant with fleshy stems or leaves.
sucker	An adventitious shoot that develops from the root of the parent plant.
suq	Arabic term for shopping area or bazaar.
swamp	A region of vegetation that develops in stagnant or slow-flowing water or on water-logged soil.
teeth	Small pointed lobes of a leaf-margin.
terete	More or less cylindrical.
terminal	Borne at the tip of a stem.
therophyte	An ephemeral or annual plant that survives adverse conditions by lying dormant as a seed.
thorn	A sharp-pointed woody projection formed from a modified reduced branch.
transpiration	The loss of water by evaporation from a plant surface, occurring mainly through the open stomata.
trifoliate*	Describes a compound leaf with three leaflets.
truncate	Squared off at the end.
tomentose	Covered with short woolly matted hairs.
tube	The united parts of a corolla or calyx.
umbel*	An inflorescence in which the flower-stalks arise from the same point at the tip of the stem to form an umbrella-like shape.
unisexual	Of one sex only.
valve	One of the parts into which a capsule or pod naturally separates at maturity.
vascular	Provided with vessels or ducts.
vegetative propagation	Non-sexual reproduction from organs such as rhizomes, stems etc. formed by the parent plant.
vein	One of the strands or bundles of vascular tissue conducting water and nutrients which form the principle framework of a leaf.
villous	With long soft unmatted hairs giving a shaggy appearance.
viviparous	Of seeds that germinate before they have been released from the parent plant.
wadi	Desert watercourse, dry except after rain.
weed	Any plant growing where it is not wanted.
whorl	A circular arrangement of more than two organs of the same kind, such as leaves, at the same level.
wing	A membranous appendage or outgrowth of certain fruits.
xerophyte	A plant adapted for growth in dry conditions.

31 spike

32 trifoliate leaf

---

* See diagram

Abbreviations
Including Authors of Plant Names
and Collectors

=	synonymous with
aff.	closely related to
Ait.	W. Aiton, 1731-1793
Ait.f.	W.T. Aiton, 1766-1849
Aitch.	J.E.T. Aitchison, 1835-1898
All.	C. Allioni, 1725-1804
Arn.	G.A.W. Arnott, 1799-1868
Asch.	P.F.A. Ascherson, 1834-1913
Benth.	G. Bentham, 1800-1884
Berth.	S.Berthelot, 1794-1880
Bertol.	A. Bertoloni, 1775-1869
Bge.	A. von Bunge, 1830-1890
B.N.H.S.	D. Phillips, (1987) Checklist of Wildflower Species (pp. 39-44) in Wildlife in Bahrain, Fourth Biennial Report. Bahrain Natural History Society, P.O. Box 20336, Bahrain
Boiss.	P.E. Boissier, 1810-1885
Bornm.	J. Bornmüller, 1862-1948
Burm.f.	N.L. Burman, 1734-1793
c	(circa) about
C.A. Mey.	C.A. Meyer, 1795-1855
Campd.	F. Campderá
Cass.	A.H.G. de Cassini, 1781-1832
Cav.	A.J. Cavinilles, 1745-1804
C.C.	Chris Cornes (member of Al Areen/Bahrain Natural History Society conservation team visiting Hawar island group January 1983 and September 1985)
cf	(confer) compare
Coss.	E.S.C. Cosson, 1819-1889
D.B.	D.A. Bellamy (1984) Additional Flowering Plants of Bahrain (pp. 90-96) in Wildlife in Bahrain, Third Biennial Report. Bahrain Natural History Society
DC.	A.P. de Candolle, 1778-1841
Dcne.	J. Decaisne, 1807-1882
Del.	A.R. Delile, 1778-1850
Desf.	R.L. Desfontaines, 1750-1833
Desr.	L.A.J. Desrousseaux, 1753-1838
Det.Au.	(determinavit) identified by author
Dum.	B.C.J. Dumortier, 1797-1878
Dum.-Cours.	G.L.M. Dumont de Courset, 1746-1824
Ed.Herb.	Collector's number of specimen collected by M. Cornes, Bahrain, 1983-86 and lodged at the Herbarium, Edinburgh Royal Botanic Garden
Ed.Rec.	Edinburgh Herbarium Records
Ehrenb.	C.G. Ehrenberg, 1795-1876
f.	(filius) son (of)
fig.	figure, illustration
flr.(flrs.)	flower, (flowers)
Forssk.	P. Forsskäl, 1732-1763
frt.	fruit
Gaud.	J.F.G.P. Gaudin, 1766-1833
Graebn.	K.O.P.P. Graebner, 1871-1933
Griseb.	A.H.R. Grisebach, 1814-1879
Guss.	G.Gussone, 1787-1866
Hasselq.	F. Hasselquist, 1722-1752
Hausskn.	H.K. Haussknecht, 1838-1903
H.B.K.	F.A. von Humbolt, A. Bonpland, C.S. Kunth
Heldr.	T. von Heldreich, 1822-1902
Hemsl.	W. Bolting Hemsley, 1843-1924
Hochst.	C.F. Hochstetter, 1787-1860
Hook.f.	J.D. Hooker, 1817-1911
Jaub.	H.F. Jaubert, 1798-1874
Johnst.	I.M. Johnstone, 1898-1960
Juss.	A.L. de Jussieu, 1748-1836
Kral.	J.L. Kralik, 1813-1892
K.V.	K.J. Virgo (1980) An Introduction to the Vegetation of Bahrain (pp. 65-109) in Wildlife in Bahrain, Annual Reports for 1978-1979. Bahrain Natural History Society
L.	C. von Linné (C. Linnaeus), 1707-1778
Lehm.	J.G.C. Lehmann, 1792-1860
L'Hér.	C.L. L'Héritier de Brutelle, 1746-1800
Loefl.	P. Loefling, 1729-1756
Lois.	J.L.A. Loiseleur-Deslongchamps, 1774-1849
M.A.	Margaret Alder, Bahrain collector 1984 onwards
M.Bieb.	F.A. Marschall von Bieberstein, 1768-1826
Medic.(Medik.)	F.C. Medicus (F.C. Medikus), 1736-1808
Mill.	P. Miller, 1691-1771
M.M.Z.	M.M. Zakis (1978) Comprehensive Study of Plant Ecology and Investigation into the Possibility of Establishing a Botanic Garden in Bahrain (pp. 14-27; translation from Arabic). University of Arab States Organisation for Arab Agricultural Development, Khartoum
Moq.	C.H.B.A. Moquin Tandon, 1804-1863
Moric.	M. Moricand, 1779-1854
non	not (of)
Oliv.	D. Oliver, 1830-1917
opp.	opposite
Pall.	P.S. Pallas, 1741-1811
Parl.	F. Parlatore, 1816-1877
P.Beauv.	A.M.F.J. Palisot de Beauvois, 1752-1820
Pers.	C.H. Persoon, 1762-1836
pl.	plant
p(p).	page(s)
Pr.Det.	provisional determination
Raf.	C.S. Rafinesque-Schmaltz, 1783-1840

Rajg.	T. Rajagopal		**Schrad.**	H.A. Schrader, 1767-1836
R.A.K.&			**Schult.**	J.A. Schultes, 1773-1831
K.J.K.	R.A. King & K.J. Kay (1984)		**Schweinf.**	G.A. Schweinfurth, 1836-1925

<table>
<tr><td>

Rajg. T. Rajagopal

R.A.K.&

K.J.K. R.A. King & K.J. Kay (1984) The Caryophyllaceae of the Arabian Peninsula, Arab Gulf Journal of Scientific Research, Vol.2, No.2. Arab Bureau of Education for The Gulf States, P.O. Box 3908, Riyadh, Saudi Arabia

Ram. Ramayya

R.Br. R. Brown, 1773-1858

Reichb. H.G.L. Reichenbach, 1793-1879

Retz. A.J. Retzius, 1742-1821

R.G. R. Good (1955) The Flora of Bahrain (pp. 126-140) in The Wild Flowers of Kuwait and Bahrain. London

Roem. J.J. Roemer, 1763-1819

Rottb. C.F. Rottboell, 1727-1797

Roxb. W. Roxburgh, 1751-1815

Sart. J. Sartori, 1809-1880

Sch.-Bip. K.H. Schultz Bipontius, 1805-1867

</td><td>

Schrad. H.A. Schrader, 1767-1836

Schult. J.A. Schultes, 1773-1831

Schweinf. G.A. Schweinfurth, 1836-1925

Sod. A.L. Sodiro, 1836-1903

Sol. D.C. Solander, 1736-1782

Sosk. G.D. Soskov

sp.,spp. species

Spr. C.P.J. Sprengel, 1766-1833

Sprun. W. von Spruner, 1805-1874

Steud. E.G. Steudel, 1783-1856

subsp.,ssp. subspecies

Sw. O. Swartz, 1760-1818

Ten. M. Tenore, 1780-1861

Thell. A. Thellung, 1881-1928

Thunb. C.P. Thunberg, 1743-1828

Trin. K.B. von Trinius, 1778-1844

var. variety

Vent. E.P. Ventenat, 1757-1808

Vierh. F. Vierhapper, 1876-1932

Viv. D. Viviani, 1772-1840

Willd. C.L. Willdenow, 1765-1812

</td></tr>
</table>

Bibliography and References

Adams, R. & M., Willens, A. & A., *Dry Lands: Man and Plants.* The Architectural Press Ltd., London

Batanouny, K.H. (1981) *Ecology and Flora of Qatar.* University of Qatar

Belgrave, J.H.D. (1975) *Welcome to Bahrain.* The Augustan Press, Manama, Bahrain

Bellamy, D.A. (1984) Additional Flowering Plants of Bahrain (pp. 90-96) in *Wildlife in Bahrain, Third Biennial Report.* Bahrain Natural History Society, P.O. Box 20336, Bahrain

Bibby, G. (1970) *Looking for Dilmun.* Collins, London

Chaudhary, S.A. (1983) *Acacia and other Genera of Mimosoideae in Saudi Arabia.* Ministry of Agriculture and Water, Riyadh, Saudi Arabia

Chaudhary, S.A., Zawawi, M.A. (1983) *A Manual of Weeds of Central and Eastern Saudi Arabia.* Ministry of Agriculture and Water, Riyadh, Saudi Arabia

Cloudsley-Thompson, J.L., Chadwick, M.J. (1964) *Life in Deserts.* Foulis, London

Cloudsley-Thompson, J.L. (1977) *Man and the Biology of Arid Zones.* Edward Arnold Ltd., London

Daoud, H.S., revised Al-Rawi, A. (1985) *Flora of Kuwait Vol. 1.* KPI, London

Frodin, D.G. (1984) *Guide to Standard Floras of the World.* Cambridge University Press

Good, R. (1954) The Bahrain Islands and Their Desert Flora (pp. 45-55) in *Biology of Deserts.* Institute of Biology, London

Good, R. (1955) The Flora of Bahrain (pp. 126-140) in *The Wild Flowers of Kuwait and Bahrain.* London

Holmes, S. (1983) *Outline of Plant Classification.* Longman, London

Heywood, V.H. (1978) *Flowering Plants of the World.* Oxford University Press

Kassas, M., Batanouny, K.H. (1984) Plant Ecology (pp. 77-90) in *Sahara Desert.* Pergamon Press Ltd., Oxford, England

Keble Martin, W. (1978) *The Concise British Flora in Colour.* Sphere Books, London

Kelly, K., Schnadelbach, R.T. (1976) *Landscaping the Saudi Arabian Desert.* Philadelphia

King, R.A., Kay, K.J. (1984) The Caryophyllaceae of the Arabian Peninsular, *Arab Gulf Journal of Scientific Research, Vol. 2, No. 2.* Arab Bureau of Education for the Gulf States, P.O. Box 3908, Riyadh, Saudi Arabia

Kwei, T. (1978) *Landscape Plants in the U.A.E.* T. Kwei, New York

Lawrence, T.E. (1935) *Seven Pillars of Wisdom.* Jonathan Cape

Lipscombe Vincett, B.A. (1977) *Wild Flowers of Central Saudi Arabia.* Milan

Mandaville Jr., J.P. (1977) Plants (pp. 229-267) in *The Oman Flora and Fauna Survey 1975, Journal Oman Studies 1.* Ministry of Information and Culture, Oman

Mandaville Jr., J.P. (1978) *Wild Flowers of Northern Oman.* Bartholomew Books, London

Migahid, A.M. (1978) *Flora of Saudi Arabia Vols. I & II.* Riyadh University, Saudi Arabia

Miller, A.G., Hedge, I.C., King, R.A. (1982) *A Botanical Bibliography of the Arabian Peninsula, Studies in the Flora of Arabia: I. Notes from the Royal Botanic Garden Edinburgh,* Vol. 40, No. 1

Morley, B.D. (1970) *Wild Flowers of the World.* Ebury Press

Phillips, D. (1987) Desert Wildflowers of Bahrain (pp. 1-44) in *Wildlife in Bahrain, Fourth Biennial Report.* Bahrain Natural History Society

Radcliffe-Smith, A. (1980) The Vegetation of Dhofar (pp. 59-86) in *The Oman Flora and Fauna Survey 1977, Journal Oman Studies 2.* Office of the Government Adviser for Conservation of the Environment, Oman

Thesiger, W. (1959) *Arabian Sands.* Longmans, London

UNESCO (1960) *Medicinal Plants of the Arid Zones.* Paris

Vesey-Fitzgerald, D.F. (1957) The Vegetation of Central and Eastern Arabia (pp. 779-798) *Journal of Ecology 45*

Virgo, K.J. (1980) An Introduction to the Vegetation of Bahrain (pp. 65-109) in *Wildlife in Bahrain, Annual Reports for 1978-1979.* Bahrain Natural History Society

Zakis, M.M. (1978) *Comprehensive Study of Plant Ecology and Investigation into the Possibility of Establishing a Botanic Garden in Bahrain* (pp.14-27, translation from Arabic). University of Arab States Organisation for Arab Agricultural Development, Khartoum

Zohary, M. (1982) *Plants of the Bible.* Cambridge University Press, Cambridge

Index of Plant Names

Page numbers for illustrations in italics

INDEX